The purpose of this fi
nductio

(Continued from front flap)

Chapter 3 develops the algebra of set operations and relates it to switching algebra. Chapter 4 provides an application to switching or logic networks.

Most of the material is relatively easy to understand, and should be suitable for individual study by engineers who want an introduction to the field.

Sets, Events, and Switching

Sets, Events, and Switching

Paul E. Pfeiffer

Professor of Electrical Engineering
Rice University

McGraw-Hill Book Company

New York   San Francisco   Toronto   London

To RUTH
and our children
·Paul, Ruth Anne, Alice, and Marilyn

SETS, EVENTS, AND SWITCHING

Library of Congress Catalog Number 63-23462

Preface

The purpose of this monograph is to provide a tutorial exposition of the material treated. The first four chapters represent an expansion and slight extension of notes developed for a course in electrical engineering analysis which is given to all undergraduate students of electrical engineering at Rice University. Approximately nine lectures in that course are devoted to the material in these chapters, although in the present extended form there is probably sufficient material for twelve to fifteen lectures. The lecture time required depends upon the mathematical maturity of the class and upon the completeness with which the topics are covered. A large portion of the material in the fifth chapter is treated briefly in a study of probability theory; this is a subsequent topic in the same course in engineering analysis referred to above.

It is hoped that the exposition provided in this book may prove useful for both classroom work and self-study, as a preparation for work in switching circuits and for a study of probability theory. The ideas presented are valuable aids to thought and analysis in many other fields, as well.

Most of the material treated herein is found in many places in the literature. There are, however, a few features of this work that may be of interest to those acquainted with the field as well as to the novice. These may be enumerated as follows:

1. The lifting of the concept of events and their occurrence out of probability theory and the application of the concept to other topics (Sec. 1-3); in particular, the viewing of logic or switching networks in terms of sets or events (Secs. 1-6, 4-1, 4-3)

2. Some features of the organization of minterm maps (Sec. 2-5)

3. Use of the indicator function to provide a tie between the algebra of set operations and switching algebra (Secs. 3-2, 3-3)

4. Use of the function designation number in binary form as a special minterm map and as a device for analyzing minority-majority logic devices (Secs. 3-5, 4-2)

5. Association of the concept of a mathematical relation with the concept of an event (Appendix II)

Even where the author may justifiably make some claim to originality, he is aware of his indebtedness to others. Anything that might be claimed as new is but an extension of or a systematic exploitation of ideas which are available in the literature. I am particularly aware of the contributions to this exposition made by Joel Howard Cyprus, former student and younger colleague. He has contributed the form of the minterm map (Sec. 2-5) exploited in this work; the use of the function designation number in binary form—the binary designator (Sec. 3-5)—as a preferred variation of the scheme used by Ledley [8]; and the analysis of minority-majority elements (Sec. 4-2).

The problems provided for each chapter vary in value and difficulty. Some of them are routine exercises to help fix procedures and concepts. Others are more interesting, either in terms of extending the material of the text or of suggesting useful applications of the ideas. It is hoped that enough problems have been provided to give some grasp of the topic to the student and to suggest to teachers other problems which may be useful. It should be pointed out that the luxuriant literature in the field abounds in problems.

I should like to add a personal word of acknowledgment and appreciation to several people who have helped bring this work into final form. Joel Cyprus has increased my indebtedness to him by joining David Allen Harris and Judd G. Stiff, Jr. in the task of reading critically the entire manuscript. I have profited from this activity—as I am sure the readers of the completed work will—although I have exercised the prerogative and responsibility of an author in persisting in my own idiosyncrasies at times. One can hardly blame them for that.

Anyone who has ever put together a book knows how much an author owes to a patient and capable secretary. Mrs. Velma T. Goodwin more than deserves my gratitude for her efforts to produce a usable manuscript.

Paul E. Pfeiffer

Contents

Introduction

The concept of a *set* and the related concepts, techniques, and strategies which make up the *theory of sets* have come to play a central role in modern mathematics. Until comparatively recently, the theory of sets was primarily the concern of specialists and of advanced students of mathematics. Its teaching was generally reserved for graduate studies. One of the features of many of the new experimental courses in mathematics at both the undergraduate and precollege levels is the strategic role of set-theoretic ideas. Some of these ideas are being introduced at the elementary school level, with even more attention at the junior high school and high school level. The theory of sets provides a way of thinking and of organizing one's thoughts that is proving effective and fruitful. The exploitation of this way of thinking is leading to more rapid development of the ability of students to handle abstract systems. Such ability is one of the characteristics of mathematical maturity.

The intuitive idea of an *event* has been given a precise meaning in modern mathematical theory of probability. The classical paper of A. N. Kolmogorov [Ref. 7, German edition], published in 1933, culminated a long development leading to a precise, axiomatic treatment of probability. The characterization of events as sets is one of the major features of this formulation. The concept of an event, so formulated, is useful in many investigations in which probability is not a subject of concern.

The symbolic representation of sets and of various operations and relations on and among sets lends itself to the algebraic manipulation of sets. The rules of set operations have long been recognized as fitting into the pattern of those systems known as *Boolean algebras*. The formal properties of such algebras were investigated by the mathematician and logician George Boole (1815–1864), after whom they are named. The concept of a Boolean algebra is an abstract one, dealing with a class of undefined objects and a pair of binary operations called Boolean "addition" and Boolean "multiplication." The algebra is grounded in a set of postulates, and it exhibits patterns of structure which make it applicable to a variety of mathematical and physical situations. In these applications or interpretations, as they are called, the elements are given specific meanings and the operations on the elements are interpreted in an appropriate manner.

Two applications or interpretations of Boolean algebra have received considerable attention from engineers. One is the *algebra of set operations*, which plays a role in the development of the mathematical theory of probability. The other is the quasi-numerical form commonly referred to as *switching algebra*. The application of this form of Boolean algebra to switching or logic networks was pioneered by Claude E. Shannon in 1938 [12]. It is in this form that the term Boolean algebra has become familiar to engineers in a variety of fields. One who is introduced to these algebras through a study of probability on the one hand and of switching theory on the other may well be at a loss to relate the two algebras, even though he may be aware that both are Boolean algebras.

Each of the factors discussed above enters into the motivation for the choice of methods and topics developed in this exposition. An immediate aim of the work is to provide a background for the study of probability theory and an introduction to work in the analysis and design of switching or logic networks. The degree of preparation provided for these two disciplines is quite unequal, however. The concept of an event as a set is carefully developed, but except for a few allusions and some simple results developed in the problems no real introduction to probability theory is given. On the other hand, enough technique and illustration is given to provide some introduction to switching theory.

The principal advantage of this treatment as background and introduction is that it ties together the algebra of set operations, the concept of events, and the ideas and techniques of switching algebra. For example, it is sometimes expedient to think of switching phenomena in the language of sets or events; at other times it is most useful to think and operate in terms of the quasi-numerical relations of the switching algebra. Also, some of the techniques developed in the applications to switching networks are equally useful in certain problems of probability theory.

At many stages of the development, the discussion is somewhat abstract and seemingly remote from application. The ideas are simple, and many engineers find them fascinating. The reader is invited to relax and enjoy the trip. If he is alert and eager, he should arrive at the destination prepared to move rapidly on the trail of engineers who have pushed into interesting and important problems.

Elements, Sets, and Classes

Chapter 1

In this chapter we consider the fundamental notions of elements, sets, and classes.   Various operations of combining sets to produce new sets are considered.   The idea of a set is related to the idea of an event. Some remarks are made concerning classes of sets and the idea of the cartesian product of sets is examined.   A number of the fundamental, abstract ideas are applied to switching or logic networks.

1-1. Fundamental Notions

The concepts of sets and elements are largely undefined—perhaps ultimately undefinable.   Yet the concepts are intuitively immediate and are taken as the starting point of a systematic discussion.   The concept of a *set* is the concept of a "collection" or "aggregate" of individual entities referred to as *elements*.   An element is a *member of a set* if it is one of the elements whose aggregate constitutes the set. Given a set, it must be possible in principle to determine whether any particular element is or is not a member of the set.   Only two possibilities are allowed: the element belongs or it does not belong; it is a member or it is not a member.

Symbols for Set Membership. It is useful to be able to operate symbolically with statements concerning sets and elements. As a first step toward the goal of an algebra of sets, we introduce a notational convention for indicating set membership. Elements are indicated by lower case letters, x, y, z, etc. Sets are designated by capital letters, A, B, C, etc. Subscripts are used in a natural and customary way. Set membership may be indicated in symbols as follows:

$x \in A$, which reads "x is a member of A" or "x belongs to A."

$x \notin A$, which reads "x is not a member of A" or "x does not belong to A."

The Universal Set. For many purposes, it is mathematically convenient to limit consideration to a specific class or set of objects. Thus, for some considerations it may be desirable to consider only positive integers, whereas for others it may be desirable to consider the set of all real numbers or the set of complex numbers. In the mathematical theory of probability, the set of all possible outcomes of a given experimental process plays an important role. Suppose a study of a coin flipping experiment is to be made. The usual approach is to consider that there are two possible outcomes of the single act of tossing a coin—usually designated heads or tails. But, physically, a third possibility may present itself: the coin may stand on edge. It must be decided beforehand whether the third condition is to be considered as a legitimate outcome, i.e., whether the experiment has been conducted successfully if the coin remains on edge.

The set of all the elements to be considered in a given investigation is often called the *universal set* and is designated by the letter U. For a given investigation we must have $x \in U$ for every element x. Because of certain natural geometric interpretations considered below, the universal set is sometimes referred to as the *basic space*.

Examples The application of set concepts to mathematical and physical investigations must start with the designation of a suitable universal set. It will be apparent that no single model uniquely describes a given situation. One of the keys to successful application lies in the ability to make an appropriate choice of elements and hence in the proper formulation of the universal set. A number of simple examples will indicate some of the possibilities. We describe the element and remark concerning the universal set.

(i) $x = $ a side of a single die as ordinarily used in games of chance. The universal set U has six elements.

(ii) $x = $ a pair of sides of a pair of dice, with each die identified. The pair of numbers $(3,2)$ may be used to represent the element consisting of the condition that side 3 shows on the first die and side 2 shows on the second die. The element $(3,2)$ is distinct from the element $(2,3)$. The universal set has 36 elements.

(iii) $x = $ a pair of numbers showing after the roll of a pair of dice. The dice are not individually identified, so that $(3,2)$ and $(2,3)$, for example, are considered to be the same element. The universal set U has 21 elements.

(iv) $x = $ a hand of r cards in a deck of 52 distinct cards, with the order of appearance unimportant. There are

$$\frac{52 \cdot 51 \cdot \cdots \cdot (52 - r + 1)}{r!} = \frac{52!}{(52 - r)!r!}$$

elements.

(v) If in example (iv) the order of drawing cards were important, the number of elements would be $52!/(52 - r)!$.

(vi) $x = $ a person residing in the United States. It is necessary to agree on how persons are to be counted, for such a universal set varies with time.

(vii) $x = $ any six-word telegram in which each word has four letters. There are 26^{24} elements. Two of these are

$$x_1 = \text{this task will help your work}$$
$$x_2 = \text{zbyx abcd efgh nnnn audr fore}$$

(viii) $x = $ any sequence of n decimal digits. There are 10^n such elements. For the case $n = 8$, two of these are:

$$x_1 = (1,2,7,3,4,2,0,0)$$
$$x_2 = (0,0,0,0,0,0,0,0)$$

(ix) $x = $ any pair of real numbers (u,v). The element x may be represented by a point in the uv plane or by the complex number $u + jv$.

(x) $x =$ any function of the form $f(t) = \alpha \sin t + \beta \cos t$. This
is an example of a *function space*. Determination of the pair
(α,β) determines an element.   Any of these functions may be
represented by the pair of numbers (α,β).

Other examples are considered throughout the text.   A very important
example for our purposes is described in the section on sets and logic
networks, below.

Designation of Sets. A set is defined or described by determining
the extent of its membership.   Nothing enters into the specification of
a set beyond the naming or determining of its members.   A set is completely identified when its members are known at least in principle.

It is often convenient to designate a set by *listing* all of the members.
For instance, the set of integers from 1 through 5 may be designated

$$A = \{1,2,3,4,5\}$$

The set of pairs of numbers (u,v) with u taking integer values 1 and 2
and with v taking integer values 1, 2, and 3 may be listed

$$B = \{(1,1), (1,2), (1,3), (2,1), (2,2), (2,3)\}$$

For more complex sets with many members, it is impractical to attempt
to list all members.   In fact, in several of the examples of universal sets
listed above, there is an infinity of members; it is thus impossible to list
them all.

It may be noted that the sets just considered are first described in
words.   They are described by certain *propositions* about the elements or
by certain *conditions*.   If an element satisfies the conditions, it is
included in the list of members.   If it does not, it is not listed as a member.   Consider the statements describing the set A.   First it is noted
that the elements are integers.   Thus, if I stands for the set of all
integers, it must be true that $x \in I$.   But not all integers are included.
Only those integers x are included for which it is true that $1 \leq x \leq 5$.
The set A could very well be indicated by the notation

$$A = \{x \in I : 1 \leq x \leq 5\}$$

which may be read: A is that set of those x in I (i.e., the set of those
integers) for which $1 \leq x \leq 5$.   In a similar way, the set B may be
designated

$$B = \{(u,v),\ u \in I,\ v \in I : 1 \leq u \leq 2;\ 1 \leq v \leq 3\}$$

If it is understood that the numbers x in the first case are taken from the set of integers (i.e., that I is the universal set), the notation could be simplified to

$$A = \{x: 1 \leq x \leq 5\}$$

Similarly for the set B, the designation may be simplified to

$$B = \{(u,v): 1 \leq u \leq 2, 1 \leq v \leq 3\}$$

These examples suggest a general scheme of notation. If x belongs to some known set of elements X and if $\pi_A(x)$ is a proposition about x which is true for those elements x in set A and is not true for elements not in set A, the set A may be designated in the form

$$A = \{x \in X: \pi_A(x)\}$$

In case X is the universal set U, it is customary to shorten the notation to

$$A = \{x: \pi_A(x)\}$$

This notation may be applied to subsets of the various universal sets listed above. To simplify reference, we use the same numbers as are found in the list above.

(iii) $A = \{x:$ sum of the numbers is 3$\}$. There is one element in this set, namely the pair (1,2).

(iv) $B = \{x:$ hand has one or more aces$\}$. It is a nice problem in combinatorial analysis to determine the number of elements in this set.

(vi) $C = \{x: x$ is male and under 40 years of age$\}$.

(viii) $D = \{x:$ no two adjacent digits are the same$\}$.

(x) $E = \{x: f(t) \leq 3\}$.

In each case, it is possible to examine an element and answer the question: Is $\pi_A(x)$ a true statement for this element?

Geometric Interpretation. It is common practice and fairly natural to represent an element in a set by a point in space. The universal set may be represented by all the points in a certain region of the plane. In the case of finite numbers of elements in the universal sets, this may be modified by considering a discrete array of points in a region in the plane. A diagram showing the universal set as a plane figure and a set of elements as a region in that set is commonly known as a *Venn dia-*

gram [14].   These diagrams are useful in illustrating certain set relationships and combinations to be considered in subsequent sections.   Figure 1-1 shows such a diagram.   Repeated use is made of such diagrams in the literature.   A number of specialized forms have been developed which have properties that are useful or expedient in various types of problems.   Some of these are discussed in later sections of this treatment.

1-2. *Elementary Set Relations and Combinations*

An element is a member of a set.   A set is a member of a class of sets. In addition to this relationship of a member to its set, there are important relationships among sets and certain combinations of sets to form new

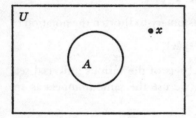

Fig. 1-1 A Venn diagram.   **Fig. 1-2** An illustration of the inclusion relation.

sets.   These are fundamental to the development of the algebra of set operations.   We consider some of the more important of these.

Inclusion. We have said above that one set is a subset of another without noting precisely what is meant by the statement.   We shall say that set A is *included in* set B or that A is a *subset* of B iffi (if and only if) each element which is a member of A is necessarily a member of B. The same thing may be expressed in symbols as follows:

$$A \subset B \text{ or } B \supset A \text{ iffi } x \in A \text{ implies } x \in B$$

The appropriateness of the terminology is indicated in the Venn diagram in Fig. 1-2.   Every point in the region representing the set A is also a point in the region representing the set B.   Thus A is inside or "included in" B in the usual sense of that term.

The inclusion relation is *reflexive*, i.e., $A \subset A$; and *transitive*, for the conditions $A \subset B$ and $B \subset C$ imply $A \subset C$ (see Fig. 1-2). If A fails to be included in B, we may on occasion write $A \not\subset B$. From the nature of the universal set, it is apparent that $A \subset U$ for each set A. The term "relation" has a precise meaning in modern mathematics, which is discussed briefly in Appendix II. For the present discussion, ordinary usage will indicate the meaning intended.

The difference between set membership and set inclusion serves to emphasize the distinction between a set $\{x_0\}$ whose only element is x_0 and the element x_0 itself. In the situation illustrated in the Venn diagram of Fig. 1-2, we may say $x_0 \in B$ and $x_0 \notin A$. It is *not* correct to say $x_0 \subset B$. What is true is that the set $\{x_0\} \subset B$, while $\{x_0\} \not\subset A$.

Proper Subsets. The inclusion relation $A \subset B$ admits the possibility that all points in set B are also in set A. If, however, there are points x in B which are not in A, this fact may be emphasized by referring to A as a *proper subset* of B. Some authors use the notation $A \subset B$ to indicate proper subsets and $A \subseteq B$ to indicate inclusion as defined above. We shall use only the symbol $\subset$, in the manner indicated in the preceding paragraphs.

Inclusion and Implication. We note in passing a fact which indicates an application of set relations to problems of logic. Suppose sets A and B are defined by propositions $\pi_A(x)$ and $\pi_B(x)$, respectively, in the manner discussed above. Then we may assert

$$A \subset B \text{ iffi } \pi_A(x) \text{ implies } \pi_B(x)$$

For example, consider a group of engineers attending a technical session. Suppose the element x is a member of this group. Let the proposition $\pi_A(x)$ be "x is a licensed professional electrical engineer"; let the proposition $\pi_B(x)$ be "x is a licensed professional engineer (any kind)." It is quite clear that if proposition $\pi_A(x)$ is true of any element x so also is $\pi_B(x)$, which is what is meant by saying the first statement implies the second. Thus, we must have

$$A = \{x: \pi_A(x)\} \subset B = \{x: \pi_B(x)\}$$

Equality. It has been emphasized that a set is characterized by its membership and by nothing else. The problem of defining or describing a set A is the problem of determining a rule whereby the elements of the universal set may be examined to discover whether or not they belong to A. This basic idea leads to the definition of *set equality* or *identity*. Two sets are *equal* iffi they have the same membership. That statement can be broken into the following two statements concerning two sets, which serve to define set equality. Two sets A and B are *equal* iffi (1) every element in A is also in B and (2) every element in B is also in A. We may write this statement in symbols as follows:

$$A = B \text{ iffi both } A \subset B \text{ and } B \subset A$$

The relation of equality is *reflexive*, since $A = A$; *transitive*, for $A = B$ and $B = C$ requires $A = C$; and *symmetric*, for $A = B$ iffi $B = A$.

If sets A and B are determined by propositions π_A and π_B, respectively, then $A = B$ iffi $\pi_A(x)$ and $\pi_B(x)$ are equivalent statements. For example, suppose the universal set is the set of real numbers x. Then

$$A = \{x: x^2 + 2 = 3x\} = B = \{x: x = 1 \text{ or } 2\} = \{1,2\}$$
$$\pi_A(x) \text{ is the statement } x^2 + 2 = 3x$$
$$\pi_B(x) \text{ is the statement } x = 1 \text{ or } 2$$

Statement π_B enumerates the *solutions* of the equation constituting π_A. For this reason, set B is sometimes called the *solution set* for the equation $\pi_A(x)$.

The Null Set. We introduce a special set which at first seems unnecessary and trivial. Its usefulness will appear as the topic is developed. The *null set* or the *empty* set is the set which has no members. The null set is designated by the symbol $\emptyset$, which is a zero with a slant line through it. Some writers use the zero symbol, for the null set plays a role somewhat parallel to the zero in ordinary algebra.

If the null set is determined by a proposition π, then $\pi(x)$ must be true of no member of the universal set. For example, if x is a hand of five cards drawn from an ordinary deck, the set of all those hands which have five aces is the null set. This is the same as saying there are no hands with five aces.

It is expedient to consider the null set as a subset of every set; i.e., $\emptyset \subset A$ for each A. Hence, $A = \emptyset$ iffi $A \subset \emptyset$. This is consistent with the previously developed idea of equality, for A can be a subset of $\emptyset$ iffi it has no members.

Union of Sets. If A and B are two sets, we may derive a new set by considering the aggregate of all elements which are members of A or of

B or of both.   This new set is called the *union* of *A* and *B*.   In symbols we write

$$A \cup B = A + B = \{x: x \in A \text{ or } x \in B \text{ or both}\}$$

For obvious reasons, the union of two sets is often referred to as the OR combination.   Two alternative notations are indicated: $A \cup B$ and $A + B$.   It is probably logically preferable to use the first symbol in order to avoid confusion of the plus sign with the sign of addition in ordinary algebra.   Because of custom in engineering works and the availability of the symbol, however, we shall frequently use the plus sign to indicate the union of sets.

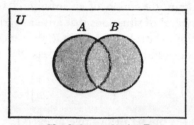

Shaded area is $A + B$

Fig. 1-3   An illustration of the union of two sets.

The union of two sets is illustrated in the Venn diagram of Fig. 1-3. The entire shaded region, consisting of the totality of the points in the region representing set *A* and of those in the region representing set *B*, constitutes the union.   Note that in the example shown some points are in both.   The formation of unions does not, however, require such an overlap of the sets.

A number of simple but important facts can be verified from the definitions by very simple reasoning.   Among these are

$$A + B = B + A \qquad\qquad A + B = B \text{ iffi } A \subset B$$
$$A + U = U \text{ for every } A \qquad A + \emptyset = A \text{ for every } A$$

The validity of the first theorem is immediately obvious.   The expression $A + B = B$ can be true iffi there are no elements in set *A* which are not also in *B*.   The expression $A + U = U$ may be viewed as a special case of the previous theorem, since every set *A* is a subset of the universal set by definition. The combination $A + \emptyset$ must consist of precisely those elements in A, since the set $\emptyset$ has no elements.

The concept of union extends immediately to a class of sets $\{A_k\}$. The *union of the class*

$$C = \bigcup_k A_k \qquad k \in I$$

is the set C consisting of all those elements which are members of at least one of the A_k. It is supposed that k runs through the values of a suitable index set I designating all the members of the class of sets. This definition includes the previous one when k has the values 1, 2 and $A_1 = A$ and $A_2 = B$.

In order to illustrate the union of an infinite class, we consider an example which is typical of situations that arise in various mathematical investigations. Suppose the basic space is R, the set of all real numbers. Thus $x \in R$ is a real number. Define the sets A_0 and A_n as follows:

$$A_0 = \{x: x < 2\} \qquad A_n = \left\{x: x \leq 2 - \frac{1}{n}\right\} \qquad n = 1, 2, \ldots$$

(i.e., the index set I is the set of positive integers).

Let $A^* = \bigcup_{n=1}^{\infty} A_n$. Then it follows that $A_0 = A^*$. To show this, we must show that $A_0 \subset A^*$ and $A^* \subset A_0$.

Suppose $x \in A^*$. Then x must belong to A_n for some particular n. For this n we have $x \leq 2 - 1/n < 2$, so that x satisfies the condition determining elements of A_0. Thus $A^* \subset A_0$.

On the other hand, if $x \in A_0$, x must have a value $2 - \epsilon$, where ϵ is a positive number. For any n such that $1/n < \epsilon$, and there is an infinity of such n, we must have $x \in A_n$ and hence belongs to the union of all the A_n. Thus $A_0 \subset A^*$, which completes the argument required to prove equality.

Intersection. If A and B are two sets, the *intersection* is the set of those elements which are members of both A and B. In symbols we may write

$$A \cap B = AB = \{x: x \in A \text{ and } x \in B\}$$

We shall generally use the simpler notation AB, although on occasion it may be desirable to use the notation $A \cap B$. The intersection combination is often referred to as the AND combination. The intersection of two sets is illustrated in the Venn diagram of Fig. 1-4. The shaded common part, consisting of the points in both the region representing set A and that representing set B, represents the new set AB.

Several facts of importance which are simple consequences of the definitions are

$$AB = BA \qquad\qquad AB = A \text{ iffi } A \subset B$$
$$A\emptyset = \emptyset \text{ for every } A \qquad AU = A \text{ for every } A$$

Again, the first theorem is immediately apparent. The intersection AB is identical with A iffi every element of A is also in B. Since $\emptyset$ has no elements, the elements common to it and to any other set do not exist.

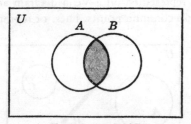

Shaded area is AB

Fig. 1-4 An illustration of the
intersection of two sets.

On the other hand A is contained in U by definition, and the result $AU = A$ follows.

The concept of intersection extends immediately to a class of sets $\{A_k\}$. The *intersection of the class*

$$D = \bigcap_k A_k \qquad k \in I$$

is the set D consisting of all those elements which are members of A_k for *every* k in the index set I.

An example similar to the one for unions above will illustrate the intersection of an infinite class of sets. As before, we suppose x is a real number and define the sets

$$B_0 = \{x\colon x \le 2\} \qquad B_n = \left\{x\colon x < 2 + \frac{1}{n}\right\} \qquad n = 1, 2, \ldots$$
$$B^* = \bigcap_{n=1}^{\infty} B_n$$

Then $B_0 = B^*$.

Obviously if $x \in B_0$, so that $x \leq 2 < 2 + 1/n$ for all n, x must belong to every B_n and hence to the intersection. Thus $B_0 \subset B^*$.

On the other hand, if $x < 2 + 1/n$ for all positive integers n, a simple argument by contradiction shows that $x > 2$ is impossible and hence $x \leq 2$, which means that $B^* \subset B_0$. The equality is thus established.

Disjoint Sets. In the definition of intersection, it is not required that there be any common elements. If two sets A and B have no elements in common, the sets are said to be *disjoint*. Thus

$$A \text{ and } B \text{ are disjoint iffi } AB = \emptyset$$

Two disjoint sets represented on a Venn diagram are characterized by no overlap—i.e., no common points, lines, or regions. This situation

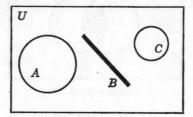

Fig. 1-5 Disjoint sets.

is illustrated in the diagram of Fig. 1-5. As a further example, the sets of real numbers defined as follows are pairwise disjoint:

$$A = \{x: x < 2\} \qquad B = \{x: 2 \leq x \leq 3\} \qquad C = \{5,7,9,13\}$$

It is customary to refer to a class $\{A_k\}$ of sets as a *disjoint class* if no two distinct sets have any elements in common. This may be expressed in symbols

$$A_k \text{ is a disjoint class iffi } A_n A_m = \emptyset \text{ for } n \neq m$$

The class consisting of the sets A, B, C, defined above, is a disjoint class.

Complement of a Set. A given set A is determined by its members. This set also determines a closely related set called the *complement* of A which consists of all those elements x which are *not* in the set A. In symbols

$$A^c = \bar{A} = {\sim}A = \{x: x \notin A\} = \{x: \pi_A(x) \text{ is not true}\}$$

We shall usually designate the complement of A by the first of the symbols shown, namely A^c, although the others are in common use in the literature.

It is sometimes desirable to think of the *relative complement* of A in the set B. This is the set of those elements which are in B but *not* in A. It is quite possible that there are no such elements, in which case the relative complement is the null set $\emptyset$. The relative complement can be expressed in terms of A^c and B as A^cB, for

$$A^cB = \{x \in B: x \notin A\} = \{x \in B: \pi_A(x) \text{ is not true}\}$$

The alternate notation $B - A$ is often used. We shall generally avoid this notation. A number of simple theorems are easily proved. Among these are

$$
\begin{array}{ll}
A^c = \emptyset \text{ iffi } A = U & A^cB = \emptyset \text{ iffi } A \supset B \\
A^c = U \text{ iffi } A = \emptyset & (A^c)^c = A \\
A + A^c = U & AA^c = \emptyset
\end{array}
$$

These theorems may be visualized readily in terms of a Venn diagram, although the logic of the argument does not depend in any way upon the pictorial representation.

Disjunctive Union. For many considerations it is useful to consider the set of elements which are in A or B but *not* in *both*. We designate such a combination by the symbol

$$A \oplus B = \{x: x \in A \text{ or } x \in B \text{ but not both}\}$$

It is readily seen that the following must hold

$$
\begin{array}{l}
A \oplus B = AB^c + A^cB = (A + B)(AB)^c \\
A \oplus B = A + B \text{ iffi } AB = \emptyset \\
A \oplus B = \emptyset \text{ iffi } A = B
\end{array}
$$

The disjunctive union is the same as the ordinary union iffi the sets are disjoint. If the sets are not disjoint, the elements in the intersection are in the union but are not in the disjunctive union. If $A = B$, there are no elements which are in A or in B but not both. This combination is often referred to as the EXCLUSIVE OR combination. Also, in mathematical books it is sometimes called the *symmetric difference*, since in terms of the minus sign it may be written

$$A \oplus B = (A - B) + (B - A)$$

An illustration of the disjunctive union is given in the Venn diagram of
Fig. 1-6.

1-3. *Sets and Events*

Much of modern probability theory is built upon a mathematical model
first developed in rigorous, axiomatic form by A. N. Kolmogorov in
1933 [7]. Fundamental to this model is the concept of the set of all
possible outcomes of a given process or experiment. This set of possible outcomes constitutes a universal set for which the individual outcomes are the elements. This universal set is called variously the
certain event (i.e., the event that is certain to occur) or the *sample space*

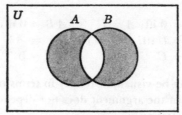

Shaded area is $A \oplus B$

Fig. 1-6 An illustration of the
disjunctive union of
two sets.

(particularly in works on statistics). The individual outcome or element is often referred to as an *elementary event*, following the terminology
of Kolmogorov.

Probability theory deals with the occurrence of events. What is
meant by an event in this theory? What is meant by the question,
"Has the event A occurred?" The question is addressed to the outcome of a trial, which is viewed as a selection of an element x from the
universal set of all possible outcomes. Occurrence or nonoccurrence
is determined by reference to some property of the elementary event
chosen. A trial is made; the outcome x is examined with respect to a
property or proposition π_A. If the proposition $\pi_A(x)$ is true, the event
A has occurred; otherwise, the event A has not occurred. The *event A*
is identified with the *set* $A = \{x: \pi_A(x)\}$. The event A occurs iffi the
element x chosen is a member of the set A.

Consider, for example, the throw of a pair of dice, with each die identified. There are 36 elementary events, namely, the 36 possible pairs of integers, each integer ranging from 1 through 6. We say that "a 5 is thrown" whenever the sum of the two numbers which turn up on a throw is 5, and similarly for other integers from 2 through 12. The event A that "a 5 is thrown" is identified with the set of four pairs $A = \{(1,4), (2,3), (3,2), (4,1)\}$. If any one of these pairs of numbers is thrown, the event A occurs. Similarly, the event B that "a 3 is thrown" is identified with the set B of two pairs $\{(1,2,) (2,1)\}$. The event C that either a 3 or a 5 is thrown is identified with the set $C = A + B$, consisting of the six pairs $\{(1,4), (2,3), (3,2), (4,1), (1,2), (2,1)\}$. The event that both a 3 and a 5 be thrown simultaneously is impossible. This is the event $D = AB$, which is the empty set, since A and B have no members in common. The empty or null set is referred to in the language of events as the *impossible event*. Two events such as A and B which have no common elements are referred to as *mutually exclusive* events.

The logical distinction between a set and an element is emphasized in Sec. 1-2. Precisely this distinction must be made between an event and an elementary event. For this reason, it is somewhat unfortunate that the elementary outcomes or possibilities are referred to as elementary events. It would be more consistent with the treatment above to use the term elementary event for that event which is the set consisting of the single possible outcome. The terminology is firmly established in the literature, however, and need cause no confusion once the situation is clearly understood.

Historically, the concept of an event as a set was formulated as a part of the mathematical theory of probability. In the intuitive thinking which led to the mathematical model of probability, the choice of the elementary event x which results in the occurrence or nonoccurrence of an event A is considered to be undetermined or "random" in some sense. In the resulting mathematical model, however, no such undefined property as "randomness" is involved. If the choice is made—in whatever manner—then a given event has occurred or not occurred, as the case may be. The concept of an event as a set is thus not limited to probability theory in any essential way. In fact, it is often helpful to use the idea in situations in which probability plays no role. For example, we find it convenient to think in such terms in dealing with logic networks.

1-4. *Classes of Sets*

In many investigations it is desirable to consider sets of sets. In order to prevent verbal confusion at this point, it is customary to refer to these as classes of sets. Sometimes the terms *collections* or *families* of sets are used. The idea of a class or a collection is not different from that of a set. Classes of sets may be indicated by script letters $\mathcal{A}$, $\mathcal{B}$, $\mathcal{C}$, etc. A set in a given class is spoken of as a *member* of the class.

A variety of notations may be used in connection with classes. It is often desirable to designate classes by listing the members. For example $\mathcal{A} = \{A_1, A_2, A_3, A_4\}$ is the class consisting of the four member sets indicated in the listing. More extensive or more general classes may be indicated with the help of the index subscripts by indicating a typical member of the set and the set of indices. The following examples should indicate the possibilities:

A finite class with n members:

$$\mathcal{A} = \{A_k\}_{k=1}^{n} = \{A_k\} \qquad k = 1, 2, \ldots , n$$

A countably infinite class

$$\mathcal{B} = \{B_k\}_{k=-\infty}^{\infty} = \{B_k\}_{k \in I} = \{B_k\} \qquad k \in I$$
$$I = \{\ldots , -3, -2, -1, 0, 1, 2, 3, \ldots\}$$

An uncountable class:

$$\mathcal{C} = \{C_\alpha\}_{\alpha \in I} = \{C_\alpha\} \qquad \alpha \in I$$
$$I = \{\alpha : 0 \leq \alpha \leq 1\}$$

In each of the last two examples, the set I is called the *index set*. One of the advantages of this notational scheme is that *subclasses* may be designated readily by taking appropriate subsets of the index set. Thus, for the class $\mathcal{B}$ we may consider subclasses by considering the index sets consisting of the positive integers, the even integers, the integers from -10 through $+12$, etc. Each of the index sets is a subset of the set I of all positive and negative integers and 0. The corresponding class is a subclass of the class $\mathcal{B}$. In particular, if $A_k = B_k$, $k = 1, 2, \ldots , n$, the class $\mathcal{A}$ is a subclass of $\mathcal{B}$.

If the index set I consists of the positive integers or of the positive integers and 0, the corresponding class is called a *sequence of sets*. It is often convenient to indicate a sequence by the notation $A_1, A_2, \ldots$ or by A_1, A_2, . . . , A_n, ... The class $\mathfrak{B}$, above, is sometimes referred to as a doubly infinite sequence. Some authors refer to class $\mathfrak{C}$ as a finite sequence.

One difference between classes of sets and sets of elements of the basic space is the nature of the members of a class. Sets may be combined to form new sets, whereas elements cannot. For example, one may start with a given class $\mathfrak{C}$ of sets. From this may be formed a new class of sets $\mathfrak{C}^*$ consisting of all finite unions of sets of $\mathfrak{C}$. Such classes of sets are important in the careful mathematical development of probability theory, although such considerations do not usually play much of a role in practical applications. Brief attention is given to some important classes in Chap. 5.

1-5. *Cartesian Product of Sets*

The set combinations studied up to this point have produced new sets of elements of the same universal set. We consider now a way of combining sets to produce sets of new, composite elements. Such a combination is called the *cartesian product of sets*, which may be defined as follows: Let A and B be two sets, with $x \in A$ and $y \in B$. The cartesian product of A and B, denoted $A \times B$, is the set of all pairs (x,y) with $x \in A$ and $y \in B$. The new set $A \times B$ thus has the elements (x,y). The sets A and B are referred to as the *coordinate sets* (or coordinate spaces) for the product set (or space) $A \times B$. The elements x and y are the *coordinates* for the element (x,y). It is customary to order the elements as indicated in the expression in parenthesis so that position identifies the coordinate space to which a coordinate belongs. It should be noted that A and B may be sets from the same universal set— in fact they may be the same set—so that the identification of the coordinate spaces is necessary.

Examples The best illustration of a product space is probably that which was first used and which is the model for the abstract concept defined above. The idea of the cartesian product of two sets is a direct generalization of the idea of ordinary cartesian coordinates of points in a plane. The scheme of identifying a point in a plane by two numbers which are the coordinates of the point is well known. Similarly, it is a standard mathematical device to represent a pair of numbers as a point in a plane which has these numbers as coordinates.

Let us examine this scheme. We begin with the representation of a

real number by a point on a line.   This idea is so familiar as to seem
"natural."   Now let us consider two sets of real numbers, R_1 and R_2,
with $x \in R_1$ and $y \in R_2$.   Actually, R_1 and R_2 are the same set—or two
"copies" of the same set.   The set of all pairs of real numbers (x,y)
is the product set $R_1 \times R_2$.   But these pairs of numbers are "naturally"
represented by points in the plane.   Thus, the cartesian product of two
lines produces the plane.   The coordinate sets, in this case, are one-
dimensional sets in space, and the product set is a two-dimensional set
in space.   Figure 1-7 illustrates this familiar situation.   It is frequently
helpful to visualize cartesian products in terms of such a geometric
representation, even in cases in which the elements of the coordinate
space may be quite abstract.

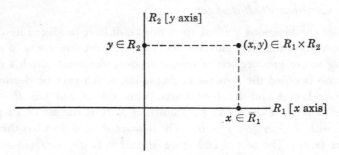

Fig. 1-7   The plane with ordinary cartesian coordinates as
an example of a cartesian product of two sets.

The concept of cartesian products can be extended to any number of
sets.   For example, the product of sets A_1, A_2, and A_3, in that order,
with respective elements x_1, x_2, and x_3, is the set $A_1 \times A_2 \times A_3$, having
as elements the triplets (x_1,x_2,x_3).   A closely related space could be
obtained by taking the cartesian product $A_1 \times A_2$ and then taking the
product of this set with A_3 to produce the space $(A_1 \times A_2) \times A_3$ with
elements $[(x_1,x_2),x_3]$.   While logically distinct from the product
$A_1 \times A_2 \times A_3$ there is a natural one-to-one correspondence between
the elements (x_1,x_2,x_3) and $[(x_1,x_2),x_3]$ which makes it convenient to
identify the two types of cartesian product spaces.

An examination of the examples of various universal sets in Sec. 1-1
shows that several of these spaces may be considered as cartesian
products of simpler spaces.   In addition to Example (ix), which is
discussed above, the following spaces are cartesian product spaces:

(ii) Each element is the pair of numbers showing on a pair of dice. Each coordinate space is the set of integers $\{1,2,3,4,5,6\}$. The coordinate spaces have six elements each and the product space has $6^2 = 36$ elements.

(vii) Each element is a six-word telegram in which each word has four letters. There are 24 coordinate spaces, each of which is the alphabet of 26 letters. There are 26^{24} elements in the product space.

(viii) Each element is a set of n decimal digits. Each coordinate space is the set $\{0,1,2,3,4,5,6,7,8,9\}$, consisting of 10 coordinate elements. There are 10^n elements in the product space.

The examples above illustrate a property of cartesian products of finite sets. If we designate by $n(A)$ the number of elements in any finite set A, we have the result that $n(A \times B) = n(A)n(B)$. The theorem may be proved by induction, starting from the fact that if each coordinate set has only one element, so also does the product space. This theorem may be extended to the cartesian product of any finite number of finite sets. Such a theorem plays an important role in developing laws of counting in the theory of permutations and combinations [4].

Repeated Trials. An appropriate product space provides a convenient model for compound experiments in which each outcome is actually a sequence (finite or infinite) of simpler outcomes. For example, suppose we consider the repeated rolling of a single die. We may be interested in the set of numbers rolled on five consecutive throws of the die. One such set is the five-tuple $(1,3,3,6,4)$. This is immediately recognized as an element of the space U which is the cartesian product $I_6 \times I_6 \times I_6 \times I_6 \times I_6$, where I_6 is the set of integers 1 through 6. Any five-tuple developed by five consecutive throws of the die is an element of the product space. The numbers are written in the order they are thrown, and the number thrown on, say, the third throw is the third coordinate of the point in the product space.

Cylinder Sets. In the consideration of any such experimental scheme (which would probably be some sort of "game of chance"), it is desirable to study various kinds of events (sets of elements). Suppose we let x be an element in U, with $x = (x_1,x_2,x_3,x_4,x_5)$, so that x_1 is the first coordinate, x_2 is the second coordinate, etc.   One type of event which is often of interest is one in which conditions are placed on one or more of the coordinates.   For example, we may be interested in the event that a 2 appears on the first or fourth throw.   This is the set of elements (five-tuples)

$$A = \{x: x_1 = 2 \text{ or } x_4 = 2\}$$
$$= \{x: x_1 = 2\} + \{x: x_4 = 2\}$$

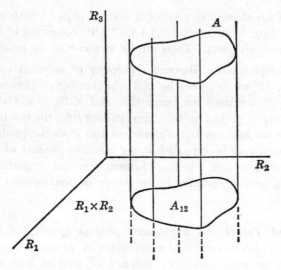

Fig. 1-8   An example of a cylinder set in three-space.

The event that a 2 appears on both the first and fourth throw would be

$$B = \{x: x_1 = 2 \text{ and } x_4 = 2\}$$
$$= \{x: x_1 = 2\} \cap \{x: x_4 = 2\}$$

In order to determine set membership, it is only necessary to examine the first and fourth coordinates.   If these have the proper values, the remaining coordinates can be anything.

Sets determined by conditions on one or several of the coordinates are often called *cylinder sets*.   The reason for this terminology can be seen in the case of three-dimensional Euclidean space which is $R^3 = R_1 \times R_2 \times R_3$ where each R_k is a set of real numbers.   Let the coordinates be x_1, x_2, and x_3. Suppose the elements (x_1,x_2) belong to a set A_{12} in the plane $R_1 \times R_2$, as sketched in Fig. 1-8. Then all points lying above and below the set A_{12} are points in the set

$$A = \{x: (x_1,x_2) \in A_{12}\}$$

The point (x_1,x_2) is a point in the plane $R_1 \times R_2$ and A_{12} is a subset of this plane.

Rectangle Sets. A special type of subset of a product space is a *rectangle set*. In the plane $R_1 \times R_2$ we may illustrate this class of sets,

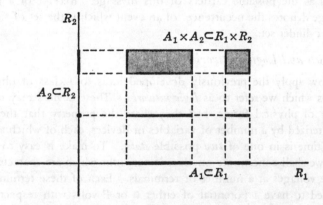

Fig. 1-9 An example of a rectangle set in the plane (two-space).

as in Fig. 1-9. If A_1 is a subset of R_1 and A_2 is a subset of R_2, then $A_1 \times A_2$ is a subset in the product space. In general, in a product space, the term rectangle set is applied to the cartesian product of subsets of the coordinate spaces.

Infinite Product Spaces. In many situations, such as a coin-flipping game or a game depending on a sequence of throws of a die, it may not be possible to specify in advance how many throws (coordinates) are needed. In this case, it is expedient to refer all events to an infinite product space, in which each element is an infinite sequence $(x_1,x_2, \ldots ,x_n, \ldots)$. Events involving only a finite number of coordinates are then dealt with as cylinder sets based on the appropriate finite product spaces. Such a device is used in certain models of com-

munication theory.   A signal source is seen as generating an infinite
sequence of letters and symbols from an alphabet (including space and
punctuation marks as letters of the alphabet).   Statistical communica-
tion theory deals with the idea of the set of all possible signals so
generated.   A given message of finite length serves to fix a certain
string of letters and hence to fix the corresponding coordinates of the
points representing possible signals.   Any signal which agrees with
the prescribed message of finite length at these coordinates is capable of
delivering the message in question.   The appearance of a message
determines a set of signals (which is a cylinder set in the sense described
above) as the possible carriers of this message.   Receipt of a given
message denotes the occurrence of an event which is the set of signals
in the cylinder set.

1-6. Sets and Logic Networks

We now apply the previously developed ideas to a class of physical
devices which we refer to as *logic networks*.   These devices may take a
variety of physical forms, but they share the property that they are
characterized by a number of variables or devices, each of which at any
given time is in one of *two* possible *states*.   To make it easy to visualize, we shall concentrate on electric networks which are characterized
by the voltages at a number of terminals.   Each of these terminals is
assumed to have a potential of either 0 or E volts with respect to a
reference.

Suppose, for example, there are three terminals marked a, b, and c, as
in Fig. 1-10.   The system has at most 2^3 states, enumerated by indicating the possible combinations of terminal voltages, as is shown in
the matrix of states in Fig. 1-10b.   Each of these states may be considered an element of the universal set of all possible states.   This is a
product space, each of whose coordinate spaces has two elements, the
voltage 0 or E.   Note that we consider the condition in which one of
the terminals has voltage $E/2$ as being impossible—in other words, if
this occurs, the system is not operating.

It is expedient to define the cylinder sets

$$A = \{x: E_a = E\} \qquad B = \{x: E_b = E\} \qquad C = \{x: E_c = E\}$$

By examination of the table of states it is apparent that each of these
sets has four elements.   For example:

$$A = \{x_4, x_5, x_6, x_7\}$$

It is natural to use the language of events in referring to these sets. Various combinations of these sets or events are readily visualized. For example:

$$A^c = \{x: E_a = 0\} = \{x_0, x_1, x_2, x_3\}$$
$$AB = \{x: E_a = E_b = E\} = \{x_6, x_7\}$$
$$AC^c = \{x: E_a = E, E_c = 0\} = \{x_4, x_6\}$$
$$ABC = \{x_7\}$$

In the physically interesting cases, not all of the states of a logic network may be physically possible. The usual situation is that the terminals are divided into two physical groups.

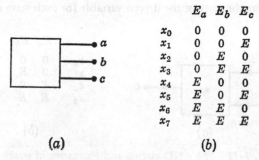

	E_a	E_b	E_c
x_0	0	0	0
x_1	0	0	E
x_2	0	E	0
x_3	0	E	E
x_4	E	0	0
x_5	E	0	E
x_6	E	E	0
x_7	E	E	E

(a)   (b)

Fig. 1-10 A logic network and a matrix of states.

1. *Driving points.* With the device considered as a unit, these points are system inputs which may be forced into any combination of the states of the individual points. If there are m of these input points, there are 2^m possible driving states.

2. *Driven points.* The states of these points are dependent upon the combinations of the states of the driving points in a manner determined by the circuit configuration.

The entire system is characterized by the combinations of the physically possible driven states associated with the 2^m driving states. Since such a device having one or more driven points has more than m points, not all of the logically conceivable states are possible. The situation may be illustrated by a consideration of three very simple logic networks which are of importance in the synthesis of more complex systems. For the present, we do not concern ourselves with the

problem of how these circuits may be realized.   We concentrate on the
description of system behavior in terms of set relations.

The AND Circuit. Consider the system indicated in block-diagram
form in Fig. 1-11*a*.   The driving points are indicated by arrows directed
toward the block representing the network.   The driven points are
identified by arrows directed outward.   Utilizing a matrix of states
similar to the one introduced in the example in Fig. 1-10, we may characterize the behavior of the system.   In this case, the matrix of states
is separated into two parts.   The columns under the voltage variables
at the driving terminals are systematically displayed in all possible
combinations in Fig. 1-11*b*.   The functional behavior of the system
is indicated by the state of the driven variable for each state of the input

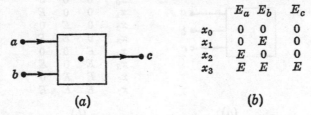

	E_a	E_b	E_c
x_0	0	0	0
x_1	0	E	0
x_2	E	0	0
x_3	E	E	E

(a)   *(b)*

Fig. 1-11   The AND circuit and its matrix of states.

variables.   If we consider each input state as an element or as an
elementary event, we may enumerate them and identify them as x_0,
x_1, x_2, x_3.
   Examination of the matrix of states shows that $E_c = E$ iffi both
$E_a = E$ and $E_b = E$.   This can be expressed simply in the symbolic
language of sets or events.   If A, B, and C are defined as in the previous
example, we must have

$$C = AB = \{x_2, x_3\} \cap \{x_1, x_3\} = \{x_3\}$$

The simple expression $C = AB$ serves to characterize completely the
input-output relations for the network.

The OR Circuit. The system described in the block diagram and the
matrix of states of Fig. 1-12 provides another element of interest.   We
may use the same set definitions as before and go immediately to a

description in the language of sets or events:

$$C = A + B = \{x_2, x_3\} + \{x_1, x_3\} = \{x_1, x_2, x_3\}$$

The reason for the term "OR circuit" should be apparent. The event C occurs iffi the event A or the event B (or both) occurs.

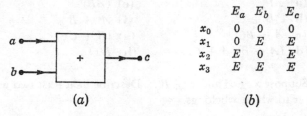

	E_a	E_b	E_c
x_0	0	0	0
x_1	0	E	E
x_2	E	0	E
x_3	E	E	E

(a)   *(b)*

Fig. 1-12 The OR circuit and its matrix of states.

The NOT Circuit. This element provides the operation of taking a complement in logic networks. As shown in the diagram and the matrix of states in Fig. 1-13, the input and output are characterized by the set relationship

$$B = A^c$$

for $E_b = E$ iffi $E_a \neq E$.

This brief treatment of logic networks represents only a first stage in the development of the topic. Except for a brief reference in Sec. 3-3,

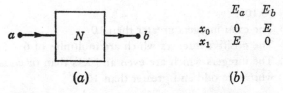

	E_a	E_b
x_0	0	E
x_1	E	0

(a)   *(b)*

Fig. 1-13 The NOT circuit and its matrix of states.

the discussion of logic networks is postponed until Chap. 4, after the development of the algebra of set operations in Chap. 3. Before turning to this algebra, however, we consider in the next chapter several important preparatory or supplementary topics.

Problems

1-1 Suppose a space U consists of the elements $\{x_1,x_2,x_3,x_4,x_5\}$. Let $A = \{x_1,x_4\}$, $B = \{x_1,x_2,x_5\}$, $C = \{x_2,x_4\}$.

Describe the following sets by listing the elements they contain:

(a) AB^c

(b) $AB + C^c$

(c) $A + BC$

(d) $(A + B)(A + C)$

(e) $(AB)^c$

(f) $A^c + B^c$

(g) $(B + C)^c$

(h) B^cC^c

1-2 Suppose $x \notin A$ and $x \notin B^c$. Describe in at least two ways the set to which x belongs.

1-3 Let the universal set U be the set of all positive integers, and consider the following subsets:

$$A = \{x: x \leq 10\}$$
$$B = \{x: x < 7\}$$
$$C = \{x: x \text{ is even}\}$$
$$D = \{x: x \text{ is odd}\}$$
$$E = \{x: x \text{ is a multiple of } 3\}$$

Express in terms of A, B, C, D, and E (and possibly their complements) the following sets:

(a) $\{2,4,6\}$

(b) $\{3,6,9\}$

(c) $\{8,10\}$

(d) The even integers greater than 10

(e) The positive integers which are multiples of 6

(f) The integers which are even and less than or equal to 6 or which are odd and greater than 10

1-4 Show by argument from definitions and derived results the validity of the following expressions, and illustrate each by the use of appropriate Venn diagrams.

(a) $A + (B + C) = (A + B) + C = (A + C) + B$

(b) $A + BC = (A + B)(A + C)$

(c) $A(B + C) = AB + AC$

(d) $(A + B)^c = A^c B^c$

(e) $(AB)^c = A^c + B^c$

(f) $A \subset B$ iffi $B^c \subset A^c$

(g) $A = B$ iffi $A^c = B^c$

(h) $A \subset B$ iffi $AB = A$

(i) $A \subset B$ iffi $AB^c = \emptyset$ iffi $A^c + B = U$

1-5 Use the results of Prob. 1-4. For each of the following expressions obtain at least two equivalent expressions which do not use the inclusion relation.

(a) $AB \subset C^c$

(b) $A + B^c \subset C$

(c) $A \oplus B \subset A^c + C$

1-6 Use the results of Prob. 1-4. For each of the following expressions obtain an equivalent inclusion relation.

(a) $(A + B^c)(C^c + D) = \emptyset$

(b) $A + BC = U$

(c) $A \oplus B = \emptyset$

1-7 A deck has 10 cards with numbers 0 through 9; i.e., each number is on one and only one of the cards. A simple game is played in which three successive draws are made. At each draw, the number on the card chosen is recorded and the card is replaced in the deck before the next draw. An elementary event thus consists of a set of three decimal digits, recorded in the order of their choice.

(a) How many elementary events are there?

(b) Let A be the event a 2 appears in the first or third place. Express event A in terms of the events B and C where B = event that a 2 appears in the first place and C = event that a 2 appears in the third place.

(c) How many elementary events does the event A comprise (i.e., how many ways can the event A occur)?

1-8 Let $\mathcal{Q} = \{A_k\}$, $k \in I$, be a class of sets and let $\mathcal{B} = \{A_k\}$, $k \in J \subset I$, be a disjoint subclass of $\mathcal{Q}$. Is the class of those A_k

not in $\mathcal{B}$ a disjoint class?   If the answer is no, give a counter-example; otherwise give a proof.

1-9   Consider a set of points A in ordinary three-dimensional Euclidean space.   This may be represented in the usual manner as a subset of the cartesian product space $R^3 = R_1 \times R_2 \times R_3$, where R_1, R_2, and R_3 are each the set (space) of real numbers. The element $x = (x_1, x_2, x_3)$ corresponds to a point in space.

(**a**) Sketch some such set A.   Then consider the set

$$B = \{(x_1, x_2): x = (x_1, x_2, x_3) \in A \text{ for some } x_3\}$$

Sketch the set B corresponding to your set A and describe it geometrically.

(**b**) Consider the set $A^\circ = B \times R_3$.   Sketch this set and describe it geometrically.

1-10   Let A and B be two rectangle sets in $U \times V$.

$$A = A_1 \times A_2 \qquad A_1 \subset U \qquad A_2 \subset V$$
$$B = B_1 \times B_2 \qquad B_1 \subset U \qquad B_2 \subset V$$

(**a**) Show that $AB = A_1 B_1 \times A_2 B_2$.   Illustrate with an example in the plane.

(**b**) Show that the rectangle set $A = A_1 \times A_2$ can be expressed as the intersection of two cylinder sets.

Functions, Partitions, and Minterm Maps

Chapter 2

In this chapter we consider first the idea of a mathematical *function* in very general but very simple terms. We then consider the idea of a *partition* of a set, which amounts to dividing the set into nonoverlapping parts, and consider a number of facts about various kinds of partitioning. One particular kind of partitioning of practical importance is represented by a special type of Venn diagram, which we refer to as a *minterm map*.

2-1. Point Functions and Set Functions

The idea of a *function* plays a central and indispensable role in mathematics. Consider the case of ordinary functions of a single real variable, where the idea is usually first encountered. The function is described or determined by one of several means: a formula, a word rule, or a "graph" of the function. Two sets of numbers are involved. One set is represented by the "argument" or the "independent variable"; the other set consists of the "values of the function." A function *f* relates one and only one value of the function to each value of the argument (in the domain of definition).   If *x* represents a value of the argument and *t* the corresponding value of the function *f*, we write

$$t = f(x)$$

The set of numbers *x* for which the function is defined is often called the *domain* of *f*; the set of all possible values of the function is called the *range* of *f*.   The function is not to be identified with its description; rather it is the *set* of all pairs of values (*x*,*t*) where *x* is from the domain and *t* is the corresponding value of the function (which is therefore in the range).   The same function may be described in several ways. Two functional descriptions represent the same function iffi they pair the same values *x* and *t*.

One of the most natural ways of expressing or describing a function *f* of a single real variable is by means of the usual graph of the function. Values of the argument are represented as points on a line, one of the coordinate axes in a plane.   At each value of the argument, the value of the function is represented by an ordinate whose length (and direction) depend upon the value of the function.   In the case of a continuous function *f*, the graph becomes a curve which describes the function.   The curve is not the function, but it serves to describe the function by telling how the values are paired.

In the case of complex numbers, this simple geometric or graphic representation of a function does not work.   Complex numbers are represented naturally and usefully by points on the "complex plane." In this situation it is natural to think of a complex function as a mapping or transformation of the *object* points on one complex plane (of which the domain of the function is a subset) to the *image* points on another complex plane (of which the range of the function is a subset). Properties of the function may be described by comparing a set of *object* points of a certain geometric figure on the plane of the domain with the corresponding configuration of *image* (or value) points on the plane of the range.   The correspondence between the various object points and the single image point corresponding to each is precisely the correspondence between argument and functional values—that is, the function.

The notion of a set of correspondences or of a mapping or transformation allows the concept of function to be extended directly to the concept of functions on abstract spaces or sets.   We consider some aspects of this extension.   Let D be some subset of the universal set U. We suppose there is a rule of correspondence which relates one and only one number t to each element x of the set D (we consider only real numbers for simplicity of exposition).

Definition: The set of all corresponding pairs (x,t) such that t is the single value associated with the element x in D constitutes a *function f* on D.   The notation

$$t = f(x) \qquad x \in D$$

indicates that t is the value of the function f at the element x (in D).

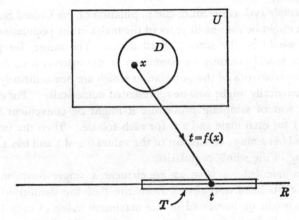

Fig. 2-1 The mapping produced by a real-valued function f whose domain is D and whose range is T.

Definition: The set D is known as the *domain* of f.

Definition: The set T of all values of t such that $t = f(x)$ for some x in D is called the *range* of f.

We take D to be a subset of U (which is possibly equal to U) and T to be a subset of R, the set of real numbers.   It is often convenient and conceptually helpful to visualize a function f in terms of a mapping from appropriate elements in the abstract space to the set of real numbers as represented by the real line.   Figure 2-1 indicates this point of view in terms of a mapping from a Venn diagram to the real line.

Examples Some elementary examples may be in order. We refer to the list of "spaces" described in Sec. 1-1. In Example (i), the case of a single die, the most natural function is the number of spots associated with the face. As we described the situation when first presented, it seems natural to consider the number as the elementary event. But in many situations, this is not adequate. The face could conceivably carry a distinct color and perhaps an imprinted number different from the number of spots. Hence it would be convenient to distinguish between the elementary event and the number associated with it. The latter defines a function of the elementary events. For an ordinary die, the range of f defined by the number of spots is the set of integers $\{1,2,3,4,5,6\}$.

In Example (vi), concerning the population of the United States, the function might be the age in years of the males in the population. The domain would be the subset of all males. The range, for practical purposes, would certainly be contained in the interval 0 to 200 years. Other characteristics of the population which are not ordinarily looked upon numerically might well be represented numerically. For example, in some sort of sampling procedure it might be convenient to write down a 1 for each male and a 0 for each female. Then the function f so defined has a range consisting of the values 0 and 1 and has a domain consisting of the whole population.

In Example (x) we have as an element a single function of the variable t (to be distinguished from the t of the definition above). Now we might be interested in the maximum value of each function in the set. This is a single number associated with the given function (i.e., the given element). Hence we have defined a function on U. Note that we have defined a function of functions. This is commonly called a *functional*. In terms of our set theory, however, each of the original functions is one of the elements of the basic space, and the single number associated with each element constitutes a value of the function defined on U.

A special function which we shall find useful in subsequent discussion is the *indicator function* or the *characteristic function* I_E of a set E. This is a function defined on U as follows:

$$I_E(x) = \begin{cases} 1, & x \in E \\ 0, & x \in E^c \end{cases}$$

Its value indicates whether or not $x \in E$. An example is the function of the population listed above, in which the number 1 is associated with each male and 0 is associated with each female. If M is the set of all males, the function defined is I_M.

The indicator function may be used to give a convenient representation of functions with a finite set of values. Suppose a function f takes on at every point of U one of the values $t_1, t_2, \ldots, t_n$. We let E_1 be the set of elements for which f has the value t_1, E_2 the set for which it has the value t_2, etc. Then it follows that the sets $E_1, E_2, \ldots, E_n$ form a disjoint class whose union is the universal set U and that f is determined by the expression

$$f(x) = \sum_{i=1}^{n} t_i I_{Ei}(x)$$

For any element x, one and only one of the indicator functions has the value unity, since x belongs to one and only one of the E_i. Suppose, for example, this were E_3. Then the indicator function for that set has the value 1 and all the other indicator functions have the value 0. The value of f is therefore t_3, as required. Functions which have a finite set of possible values (i.e., the range has only a finite number of points) are often referred to as *simple functions*. The ideas above may be extended to functions which have a countably infinite set of distinct values.

Inverse Functions. Closely related to the idea of a function is that of the inverse of a function. The idea can be visualized best in terms of the mapping concept as applied to functions. In the definition of a function, it is emphasized that to each element x in the domain D there corresponds one and only one element t in the range T. It is not necessary, however, that to each t there correspond only one x. In general, to each t in T there will correspond a set of x such that $t = f(x)$. In the direction of the reverse or inverse mapping, the correspondence is between elements t and subsets of D.

Definition: If f is a function whose domain is D ($x \in D$) and whose range is T ($t \in T$), the *inverse function* f^{-1} is the set of correspondences between each t in T and the subset of D which is mapped into t by f. We designate the latter set by

$$f^{-1}(t) = \{x \in D : f(x) = t\}$$

If for each t in T there is one and only one x in D, the inverse function is a function and f and its inverse f^{-1} are said to be *one-to-one*.

As an example, consider the indicator function I_A for a set A. The domain D is the whole space U, and the range T is the two points 0 and 1. This function has a very simple inverse: $I_A^{-1}(1) = A$ and $I_A^{-1}(0) = A^c$. The indicator function is, therefore, not one-to-one, because every element in A is mapped into the number 1 and every point in the set A^c is mapped into the number 0. On the other hand,

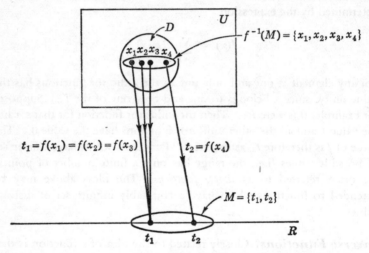

Fig. 2-2 The inverse image of a set of points under the inverse mapping f^{-1}.

the function defined as the number of spots on the face of a single die is a one-to-one function from the universal set of elements corresponding to the various faces and to the set of integers $\{1,2,3,4,5,6\}$. The simple function described above with range $T = \{t_1, t_2, \ldots, t_n\}$ has the inverse described by $f^{-1}(t_i) = E_i$ for each $i = 1, 2, \ldots, n$.

Once the inverse function is introduced as a mapping, it is convenient to extend the notation indicating the object set in the following manner. Let M be some subset of the range T. Then we let

$$f^{-1}(M) = \{x \in D : f(x) \in M\}$$

The *inverse image* of any subset M of the range is the set of all those x for which the value $f(x)$ is a point in M. Figure 2-2 shows a schematic representation of the inverse image produced by f^{-1}. It is supposed that f maps the three points x_1, x_2, x_3 and no other into the point t_1. It maps the point x_4 and no other into t_2. If we let $M = \{t_1, t_2\}$, then $f^{-1}(t_1) = \{x_1, x_2, x_3\}$, $f^{-1}(t_2) = \{x_4\}$, and $f^{-1}(M) = \{x_1, x_2, x_3, x_4\}$.

Point Functions. The functions defined above are often referred to as *point functions* to distinguish them from other types of functions on the same spaces. The concept of point functions (and their inverses) is important in the theory of probability. In many applications of probability theory, numbers are associated with the outcomes of a trial (i.e., the elementary events). These numbers may then be considered values of a function defined on the elementary events (elements of the basic space). When certain "measurability" conditions are met, so that appropriate probability statements can be made about sets of values of such a function, the function is called a *random variable*. Although a description of these measurability conditions would carry us beyond the scope of the present discussion, the concept is fairly simple in terms of the mapping ideas presented above.

Set Functions. In dealing with sets, it is often desirable to associate a number with each set of a certain class. For example, in dealing with finite sets it is natural to associate with a given set A the number $n(A)$ of elements in the set. Or one may be interested in the average age of that subset of the male population which attends a given college. In such cases, we associate a number with a set, so that we have defined a *set function*. One of the very important examples of a set function is the *probability function* which associates a number between 0 and 1 with each event (i.e., with every set of elementary events).

Viewed from the standpoint of the universal set whose elements make up the sets upon which the function is defined, a set function must be distinguished from a point function. The sets upon which the function is defined form a class (set) of sets. The function is thus defined on members (elements) of the class (set) of sets. Viewed from the standpoint of this class, the set function has the same character as a point function on the universal set. Thus, no really new concept has been introduced. We shall not pursue this matter further, for it is usually easier to distinguish between point functions and set functions—in fact, it is necessary to do so if both are used in the same investigation.

2-2. Partitions

A finite or countably infinite class $\mathcal{P}(E)$ of disjoint sets E_i whose union is the set E is known as a *partition of the set E*.   If E is the universal set, we simply refer to $\mathcal{P}(U)$ as a *partition* $\mathcal{P}$.   In the partition $\mathcal{P}(E)$ of E, each element x in E is a member of one and only one of the sets E_i.   It is convenient to refer to the sets E_i as *cells*.   In the language of events, a partition $\mathcal{P}$ is a class of mutually exclusive events, one of which is sure to occur.   Such a class is sometimes referred to as a *complete system of events*.   A partition $\mathcal{P}(E)$ of the set E divides the Venn-diagram representation of the set E into nonoverlapping sectors which cover the entire set.   The simplest nontrivial example of a partition is the pair of sets A and A^c, where A is a nonempty proper subset of the universal set U.

It is apparent that the intersections of a set E with the members of a partition $\mathcal{P}$ form a partition $\mathcal{P}(E)$ of the set E.   Only nonempty sets E are of interest.   In fact, the interesting cases usually consist of those in which two or more members of the resulting partition $\mathcal{P}(E)$ are nonempty.

The following statements about partitions extend immediately to the partitions of a nonempty set E.   Nothing essential is lost for most purposes if the empty cells of a partition are discarded.   The remaining cells form a partition which may be referred to as the *nonempty part* of $\mathcal{P}$. If a partition has no empty cells (i.e., is identical with its nonempty part), we refer to it as a *nonempty partition*.

Consider two partitions $\mathcal{P}_1$ and $\mathcal{P}_2$ with cells A_i, $i = 1, 2, \ldots, m$ and B_j, $j = 1, 2, \ldots, n$, respectively.   The partition $\mathcal{P}_2$ is called a *refinement* of $\mathcal{P}_1$ iffi each cell B_j is a subset of some cell A_i.   In this case, we may write $\mathcal{P}_2 \le \mathcal{P}_1$.

The class of sets of the form A_iB_j, where i and j run through the set of permissible indices, forms a new partition called the *joint partition* $\mathcal{P}_1\mathcal{P}_2$ or the *product partition*.   It is apparent that $\mathcal{P}_2\mathcal{P}_1$ is the same as $\mathcal{P}_1\mathcal{P}_2$.   The concept may be extended to the product of any finite number of partitions.   It is also apparent that a joint partition is a refinement of each of the partitions in the product; and if $\mathcal{P}_2 \le \mathcal{P}_1$, it is apparent that $\mathcal{P}_1\mathcal{P}_2 = \mathcal{P}_2$.

Fundamental Partitions for Discrete Sets.   In the case where the universal set U consists of a finite number of elements $x_1, x_2, \ldots,$

x_n, it is often convenient to deal with what we may call the *fundamental partition* for the discrete set. For each index k we let E_k be the set $\{x_k\}$ consisting of the single element x_k. The class of sets $\{E_k\}$, $k = 1, 2, \ldots, n$, forms a partition. Any nonempty subset of U is thus a disjoint union of members of the fundamental partition. The concept can be applied as well to discrete sets consisting of a countable infinity of elements.

Partitions Generated by a Class. Any class of a finite number of distinct sets *generates* a partition. This type of partition is of considerable interest in subsequent developments. We may illustrate by considering three sets A, B, and C, from which we form all the possible intersections or product sets obtained by intersecting either A or A^c with B or B^c and C or C^c. There are eight of these sets which may be tabulated as follows:

$$\begin{array}{ll} A^cB^cC^c & A\ B^cC^c \\ A^cB^cC & A\ B^cC \\ A^cB\ C^c & A\ B\ C^c \\ A^cB\ C & A\ B\ C \end{array}$$

From the properties of intersections and complements, it is easily seen that the intersection of any two of these product sets is empty. Any element x may be assigned to one and only one of the sets by determining the answers to the three questions: Does it belong to A? Does it belong to B? Does it belong to C? For example, if the answers are yes, no, yes, respectively, the element in question belongs to AB^cC. The eight product sets thus form a partition. It is apparent that this partition is the joint partition formed by the product of the simple partitions $\{A,A^c\}$, $\{B,B^c\}$, and $\{C,C^c\}$. We may speak quite naturally of this partition as the *partition generated by the class of sets A, B, C*, and refer to the sets A, B, C as *generating sets*. For reasons that appear below, the cells for this partition are referred to as *minterms*. We use the expression minterm to refer both to the cell and to the literal expression representing the cell. Figure 2-3 shows a Venn diagram representing the minterms for the partition generated by the sets A, B, C. The case illustrated has all three of the generating sets intersecting. In case two or more of the generating sets are disjoint, some of the minterms will be empty (impossible events). If the generating sets themselves form a partition $\mathcal{P}$, the nonempty part of the partition generated will be identical with $\mathcal{P}$. The reader should sketch various cases to get an insight into the possibilities.

It is obvious that partitions may be generated by any finite class $\{A_0, A_1, \ldots, A_N\}$ of $N + 1$ distinct generating sets. Each minterm consists of $N + 1$ factors. There are two choices for each factor. Hence there are 2^{N+1} distinct (and disjoint) minterms. Since each element of the space must be in one—and because of the disjoint character only one—of the minterms, the class of minterms is a partition. This partition is the product partition for the $N + 1$ partitions $\mathfrak{A}_0, \mathfrak{A}_1, \ldots, \mathfrak{A}_N$, where $\mathfrak{A}_k$ is the partition $\{A_k, A_k{}^c\}$ for each $k = 0$, $1, \ldots, N$. It is shown in a later section that any set derived from the

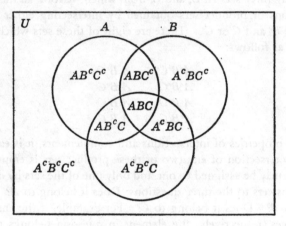

Fig. 2-3 Venn diagram showing regions representing various minterms for three variables.

class of generating sets by the processes of taking unions, intersections, and complements may be expressed as the union (necessarily disjoint) of an appropriate set of minterms. The importance of this fact appears in the subsequent development.

2-3. Simple Functions and Partitions

In Sec. 2-1, the concept of a *simple function* is presented. Such a function f defined over the whole space U or some suitable subset E is characterized by a range consisting of a finite number N of possible values,

$\{t_1, t_2, \ldots, t_N\}$. If for each $i = 1, 2, \ldots, N$ we let

$$E_i = \{x : f(x) = t_i\}$$

then we must have

$$E_i E_j = \emptyset \qquad i \neq j \qquad \text{and} \qquad \bigcup_{i=1}^{N} E_i = E \text{ (or } U)$$

Thus the E_i form a partition $\mathcal{P}(E)$ of the domain of f. In the discussion to follow, we shall assume that E is the whole space. Obvious modifications of the statements can be made for a restricted domain.

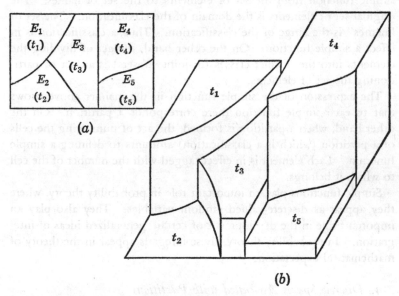

Fig. 2-4 A simple function as a step function.

Step Function. It is interesting to note that a simple function is a generalization of the idea of a step function. If the space U and the cells E_i can be represented in terms of nonoverlapping regions such as is shown in Fig. 2-4, the step function is constant over each of the cells. If the function is represented as a surface in the manner customary in dealing with ordinary functions over a plane set, the surface has the step character, jumping sharply at the boundaries from one value to another. The principal difficulty with this representation is indicating to which of the cells the boundary curves belong. This need cause no real difficulty, since the use of such diagrams is schematic and is intended as an aid to mental visualization.

Classification. The simple function is closely related to the idea of the classification of the elements of some set. To each member or element of this set there is assigned a "class." This may be viewed as putting this element into a particular subset. Each element goes into one and only one such subset. To each such subset may be assigned a name (which may be a number). This is precisely the idea of a simple function from the set of elements to the set of names. The original set of elements is the domain of the classification. The set of "names" is the range of the classification. Thus, a classification is in effect a simple function. On the other hand, the act of dividing the elements into the distinct classes (disjoint subsets) is an act of partitioning the set of elements.

The expression of the simple function in the manner above shows that to each simple function there corresponds a partition. On the other hand, when a partition is formed, the act of numbering the cells of a partition (which is a classification) amounts to defining a simple function. Each element is in effect tagged with the number of the cell to which it belongs.

Simple functions play an important role in probability theory, where they appear as discrete-valued random variables. They also play an important role in the development of certain generalized ideas of integration. In probability theory, these integrals appear in the theory of mathematical expectation.

2-4. *Discrete Spaces Associated with Partitions*

In many investigations, the cells of a partition provide the "smallest" subdivisions of the basic space to be considered. Some authors refer to these fundamental events (i.e., the cells) as elementary events. Such usage confuses the distinction between elements (elementary events) and sets (events). In order to bring clarity and precision to such discussions, it is often convenient to consider a discrete space associated with the partition, as follows:

To a given partition $\mathcal{P}$, we relate a discrete space

$$D = \{d_1, d_2, \ldots, d_N\}$$

by setting up the correspondence

$$E_k \sim D_k = \{d_k\} \qquad k = 1, 2, \ldots, N$$

so that
$$D = \bigcup_{k=1}^{N} D_k = \{d_1, d_2, \ldots, d_N\}$$

If $\mathcal{P} = \{E_1, E_2, \ldots, E_N\}$ is the partition associated with a simple function f, as discussed in Sec. 2-3, this function may be replaced by a new function g on D by setting

$$g(d_k) = t_k \qquad k = 1, 2, \ldots, N$$

If the t_k are distinct, as we have tacitly assumed above, the function g is one-to-one.

Suppose we have two partitions $\mathcal{P}_1$ and $\mathcal{P}_2$ to which we make correspond the discrete spaces X and Y, respectively. Then it is convenient to make the discrete space $X \times Y$ correspond to the product partition $\mathcal{P}_1 \mathcal{P}_2$.

Consider

$$\mathcal{P}_1 = \{E_1, E_2, \ldots, E_N\} \sim X = \{x_1, x_2, \ldots, x_N\}$$
$$\mathcal{P}_2 = \{F_1, F_2, \ldots, F_M\} \sim Y = \{y_1, y_2, \ldots, y_M\}$$
$$\mathcal{P}_1 \mathcal{P}_2 = \{E_i F_j\} \sim X \times Y = \{(x_i, y_j)\}$$
$$1 \leq i \leq N \qquad 1 \leq j \leq M$$

The product partition has $N \cdot M$ cells, and the product space has an equal number of elements, properly indexed to make the correspondence evident. It is apparent that this scheme may be extended to the product of any number of partitions.

For the partition generated by a class of sets $\{A_N, A_{N-1}, \ldots, A_0\}$, one particular representation is of interest. This partition is the product partition $\mathcal{Q}_N \mathcal{Q}_{N-1} \cdots \mathcal{Q}_0$, where $\mathcal{Q}_k = \{A_k{}^c, A_k\}$, $0 \leq k \leq N$. To the partition $\mathcal{Q}_k$ we make correspond the *binary space* $B_k = \{0,1\}$, with $A_k{}^c$ corresponding to 0 and A_k corresponding to the element 1. In the binary product space $B^{N+1} = B_N \times B_{N-1} \times \cdots \times B_0$, the element corresponding to a minterm is an $N + 1$-tuple of 0s and 1s. The kth coordinate is 0 if the factor $A_k{}^c$ is present in the minterm, and this coordinate is 1 if the factor A_k is present. The coordinates are numbered 0 through N, starting from the right, in this scheme. For example, if $N = 3$, the element $(0,1,1,0)$ corresponds to the minterm $A_3{}^c A_2 A_1 A_0{}^c$. Figure 2-5 shows a geometric representation in the case

$N = 2$ (3 coordinates). Each coordinate space $\mathcal{B}_k$ consists of two points on the real line, namely, 0 and 1. The product space consists of $2^{N+1} = 8$ points as shown. Coordinates for each of the points are indicated on the diagram.

2-5. Minterm Maps

The Venn diagram of Fig. 2-3 provides a somewhat cumbersome representation of the partition generated by sets A, B, C. The situation becomes quite complex as the number of generating sets increases.

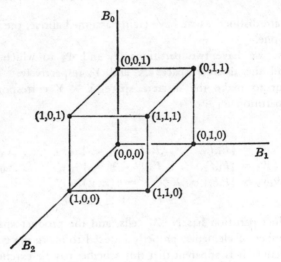

Fig. 2-5 Discrete product space corresponding to the partition generated by three sets.

For the representation of partitions generated by classes of sets, a special form of the Venn diagram, commonly referred to as a *minterm map*, is quite useful. These maps are associated in the engineering literature with the names of E. W. Veitch and M. Karnaugh, whose use of them in the early 1950s popularized slightly different versions. The version developed here was suggested to the writer by Joel H. Cyprus, who subsequently discovered that Venn had reported it in his book [Ref. 14, chap. 5] in 1894 as the invention of H. Marquand in 1885!

We begin by considering the minterms constructed from the sets A_2, A_1, A_0, considered systematically in that order. The Venn diagrams in Figs. 2-6*a*, *b*, and *c* show particular choices of the regions to represent the generating sets. The fact that the set A_1 is represented by a pair of subregions need cause no concern, for the idea of set has nothing to do with the geometric idea of continuity. If these sets are represented on a single diagram, as in Fig. 2-6*d*, the universal set is divided into eight subsets represented by eight rectangular regions. Each of these regions must represent one of the minterms. The name

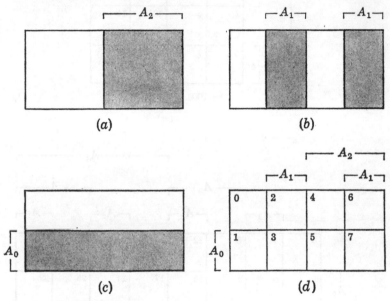

Fig. 2-6 Development of the minterm map for three variables.

minterm is derived from the fact that a *min*term corresponds to the *minimal* region on the map or diagram.

The particular scheme shown has the advantage of arranging the minterms in a systematic fashion in keeping with an ingenious and useful way of numbering the minterms. This method makes use of a representation of each minterm as a binary number, for which the decimal equivalent is then derived. The representation is as follows. The generating sets are kept in the order A_2, A_1, A_0. If the first set in the minterm is A_2, the first number in the binary representation is a 1, otherwise it is a 0. Similarly, 1s or 0s in the second and third places indicate whether the corresponding generating set or its complement is

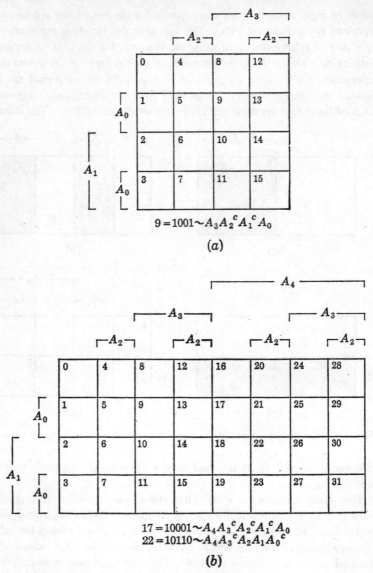

$$9 = 1001 \sim A_3 A_2{}^c A_1{}^c A_0$$

(a)

$$17 = 10001 \sim A_4 A_3{}^c A_2{}^c A_1{}^c A_0$$
$$22 = 10110 \sim A_4 A_3{}^c A_2 A_1 A_0{}^c$$

(b)

Fig. 2-7   Minterm maps for *(a)* four variables and *(b)* five variables.

present. The scheme may be illustrated by tabulating the minterms, their binary representations, and the decimal equivalent as follows:

$$A_2^c A_1^c A_0^c \sim 000 = 0 \qquad A_2 A_1^c A_0^c \sim 100 = 4$$
$$A_2^c A_1^c A_0 \sim 001 = 1 \qquad A_2 A_1^c A_0 \sim 101 = 5$$
$$A_2^c A_1 A_0^c \sim 010 = 2 \qquad A_2 A_1 A_0^c \sim 110 = 6$$
$$A_2^c A_1 A_0 \sim 011 = 3 \qquad A_2 A_1 A_0 \sim 111 = 7$$

The minterms on the diagram of Fig. 2-6d are numbered according to this scheme. A careful check will show that the square numbered 5 is indeed in A_2, not in A_1, and in A_0. Other minterms may be checked accordingly. The binary representation of the minterm corresponding

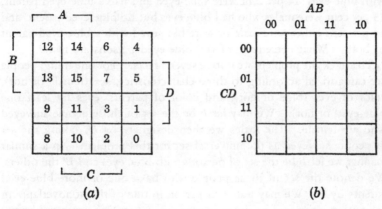

Fig. 2-8 Minterm maps in four variables as arranged by (a) Veitch and (b) Karnaugh.

to a block on the diagram can be determined by asking systematically: Does it belong to A_2? Does it belong to A_1? Does it belong to A_0? In each case, if the answer is yes, record a 1. If the answer is no, record a 0. The resulting string of 1s and 0s is the binary representation.

It should be apparent that the numbering scheme can be extended to minterms developed on any number of generating sets. Also, a comparison of the binary representation with the coordinates of the points in the binary-product-space representation developed at the end of the previous section shows their direct correspondence. The minterm maps of Figs. 2-7a and b illustrate the orderly arrangement of minterms for four and five variables. An obvious rearrangement would put the minterms in numerical order across the diagram in rows instead of vertically in columns. Figs. 2-8*a* and *b* show the arrangement of minterms for four variables in the maps due to Veitch and to Karnaugh, respectively. For some purposes, one or the other of these arrangements may be preferable.

As an example of one use of minterm maps, we may consider the following problem in fractional relationships, which is expressed as a problem in genetics but which has analogs in many different practical situations.

Problem. In a study of genetics, the following data were found. Of the people surveyed, 52 per cent were female, 24 per cent were female with blue eyes, 14 per cent were blue-eyed and had a blue-eyed parent, 13 per cent were males who had blue eyes but no blue-eyed parent, and 54 per cent either were male or were blue-eyed with a blue-eyed parent or both. What percentage of the blue-eyed persons are male?

To attack the problem we notice several facts. For one thing, people are categorized according to three characteristics, sex (female or not), color of eyes (blue or not), and color of parents' eyes (at least one blue-eyed or not). We may let F be the set of those people surveyed who are female. The males we then designate by F^c, taking the set of people surveyed as the universal set for this problem. In a similar manner we let B be the set of persons with blue eyes and B^c the others. We denote the set of those people who have one or more blue-eyed parents by P. We may put each person in one of the nonoverlapping categories designated by the minterms in the partition generated by the class F, B, P. Any set of persons determined by the three categories is then a union of appropriate minterms. The percentage in such a set is the sum of the percentages in the minterms included in the union.

Suppose the minterms are represented on the minterm map of Fig. 2-9. For minterm numbered k we let p_k be the percentage of people surveyed who fall in that category. We let $p(A)$ be the percentage of people in set A. We may use the data given and the minterm map to show that

$$p(F) = p_4 + p_5 + p_6 + p_7 = 52$$
$$p(FB) = p_6 + p_7 = 24$$
$$p(BP) = p_3 + p_7 = 14$$
$$p(F^cBP^c) = p_2 = 13$$
$$p(F^c + BP) = p_0 + p_1 + p_2 + p_3 + p_7 = 54$$

The desired percentage is the ratio

$$p(F^cB)/P(B) = (p_2 + p_3)/(p_2 + p_3 + p_6 + p_7)$$

The data above plus the fact that the percentages in all minterms must add to 100 give a set of algebraic equations which may be solved by purely algebraic means for the desired combinations. We note that the percentage in the complement of a given set A must be $100 - p(A)$. The algebraic procedure may be simplified greatly by utilizing the minterm map. The problem is solved readily if $p_2 + p_3$ is determined.

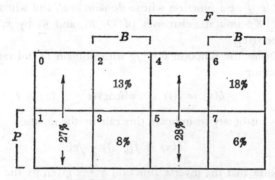

Fig. 2-9 Minterm map representation of percentages of persons in various categories according to three characteristics: F = female, B = persons with blue eyes, and P = persons with one or more blue-eyed parents.

To do this, it is only necessary to determine p_3, since p_2 is given. Inspection of the minterm map shows that

$$p_7 = p(F^c + BP) - p(F^c) = 54 - (100 - 52) = 6$$

We may then use the data to see that $p_3 = 14 - 6 = 8$. Thus $p_2 + p_3$ is 21. The solution to the problem is $21/45 = 46.7$ per cent. If other combinations are desired, the data may be used to determine percentages for various minterms or combinations thereof. The percentages which may be deduced from the data are shown on the minterm map of Fig. 2-9. More data are needed to resolve the percentages in the two pairs $p_0 + p_1$ and $p_4 + p_5$. It should be noted that the use of minterm maps and the associated set theory is not necessary for the solution of the problem.   The organization of the data achieved by this scheme, however, is extremely useful.

Problems

2-1 Show that a real-valued function f on space U is an indicator function iffi for each positive integer n it is true that the nth power f^n is equal to the function f.

2-2 Let g be a function whose domain is D and whose range is R_1; and let f be a function whose domain is R_1 and whose range is R_2. We indicate elements of D, R_1, and R_2 by x, t, and u, respectively.

Define the function $h = fg$ with domain D and range R_2 by requiring

$$h(x) = f(t) \qquad \text{whenever} \qquad g(x) = t$$

It is customary to indicate this rule by the notation

$$h(x) = f[g(x)] = fg(x)$$

Show that the inverse function h^{-1} is given by the rule

$$h^{-1}(M) = g^{-1}(N) \qquad \text{whenever} \qquad f^{-1}(M) = N$$

This is usually written

$$h^{-1}(M) = g^{-1}[f^{-1}(M)] = g^{-1}f^{-1}(M)$$

Illustrate by representations similar to that in Fig. 2-2.

2-3 A set function $m(\cdot)$ defined on a class $\mathcal{C}$ of sets is said to be *additive* if, whenever A and B are disjoint members of the class whose union $A + B$ is also a member, we have

$$m(A + B) = m(A) + m(B)$$

Show that if $m(\cdot)$ is a finite-valued, nonnegative, additive set function on a class $\mathcal{C}$ which contains the empty set $\emptyset$, then $m(\emptyset) = 0$. (Note that $\emptyset$ has no members in common with any set A and that $A + \emptyset = A$.)

2-4 If U is a finite set, the function $n(\cdot)$ defined on the class $\mathcal{Q}$ of all subsets of U by the rule

$$n(A) = \text{number of elements in set } A$$

is a finite-valued, nonnegative, additive set function on $\mathcal{Q}$.

(a) Show that for any two sets A and B,

$$n(A + B) = n(A) + n(B) - n(AB).$$

(b) Show that $n(A^c) = n(U) - n(A)$.

(Suggestion: Write $A = AB^c + AB$ and do the same for B and $A + B$. Use the fact that the minterms are disjoint).

2-5 Let U be a finite sample space with N elements. The class $\mathcal{Q}$ of all subsets A is the class of events. Let $n(\cdot)$ be the set function defined in Prob. 2-4. Then the *classical probability* function $P(\cdot)$ is the set (event) function defined by the rule

$$P(A) = \frac{n(A)}{N}$$

Show that $P(\cdot)$ satisfies the following rules.

  (i) $P(U) = 1$
 (ii) $P(A) \geq 0$
(iii) If A and B are disjoint (mutually exclusive events), $P(A + B) = P(A) + P(B)$.

2-6 Let m be any finite-valued, nonnegative, additive set function defined on the class $\mathcal{Q}$ of all subsets of a finite space U. Consider the new function $P(\cdot)$ defined on $\mathcal{Q}$ by the rule

$$P(A) = m(A)/m(U) \qquad m(U) > 0$$

(a) Show that $P(\cdot)$ has the properties (i), (ii), and (iii) of the classical probability function described in Prob. 2-5.

(b) Any additive set function $P(\cdot)$ defined on $\mathcal{Q}$ and having properties (i), (ii), (iii) of the classical probability function is called a *probability measure*. Show that any probability measure $P(\cdot)$ has the additional properties

    (iv) $P(A^c) = 1 - P(A)$
    (v) $P(\emptyset) = 0$
    (vi) $P(A) = P(AB) + P(AB^c)$
    (vii) $P(A + B) = P(A) + P(B) - P(AB)$
    (viii) If $A \subset B$, $P(A) \leq P(B)$
    (ix) If $\{A_i\}$ $i = 1, 2, \ldots, n$ is a disjoint class,

$$P(\bigcup_{i=1}^{n} A_i) = \sum_{i=1}^{n} P(A_i)$$

2-7 Let AB be a nonempty intersection of two sets A and B, and let $\mathcal{P}(A) = \{A_1, A_2, \ldots, A_n\}$ be a partition of the set A. Show that the class $\{A_1B, A_2B, \ldots, A_nB\}$ is a partition of the intersection AB.

2-8 Suppose $A \times B$ is a rectangle set in the cartesian product space $U \times V$, with $A \subset U$ and $B \subset V$.

(a) Show that $A \times B$ may be expressed as the intersection of two cylinder sets. Illustrate with a rectangle set in the plane.

(b) Suppose $\mathcal{P}(A) = \{A_1, A_2, A_3\}$ is a partition of set A. Show that $\{A_1 \times B, A_2 \times B, A_3 \times B\}$ is a partition of $A \times B$.

2-9 Show that the product of the partition generated by the class $\{A,B,C\}$ with that generated by the class $\{D,E\}$ is the partition generated by the class $\{A,B,C,D,E\}$.

2-10 Consider the elementary functions f and g defined by

$$f(x) = 0 \cdot I_A(x) + 1 \cdot I_B(x)$$
$$g(x) = 0 \cdot I_C(x) + 1 \cdot I_D(x) + 3 \cdot I_E(x)$$

where $\{A,B\}$ and $\{C,D,E\}$ are partitions. Then

$$A = \{x : f(x) = 0\}, E = \{x : g(x) = 3\}, \text{etc.}$$

(a) Show that the sum $f + g$ of the two functions f and g is given by the formula

$$f + g = 0 \cdot I_{AC} + (I_{AD} + I_{BC}) + 2 \cdot I_{BD} + 3 \cdot I_{AE}$$
$$+ 4 \cdot I_{BE}$$

(b) Derive a corresponding formula for the product $f \cdot g$ of the two functions f and g.

(c) Write a formula for the square g^2 of the function g.

Note: Problem 2-11 has general formulas including the above as special cases. Make direct derivations above, but use the general formulas of Prob. 2-11 to check your results.

2-11 Let f and g be two simple functions given by the expressions

$$f = \sum_{i=1}^{n} t_i I_{A_i} \qquad g = \sum_{j=1}^{m} u_j I_{B_j}$$

where $\{A_i\}$ and $\{B_j\}$ are partitions and $\{t_i\}$ and $\{u_j\}$ are sets of real numbers. Let $r(\cdot)$ be a function of a single real variable and let $h(\cdot \ \cdot)$ be a function of a pair of real variables. Show that

(a) $r[f(x)] = \displaystyle\sum_{i=1}^{n} r(t_i) I_{A_i}(x)$

(b) $h[f(x), g(x)] = \displaystyle\sum_{i=1}^{n} \sum_{j=1}^{m} h(t_i, u_j) I_{A_i B_j}(x)$

2-12 Consider the simple function f given by

$$f = a I_A + b I_B + c I_C$$

We consider the partition generated by the class $\{A, B, C\}$ and write

$$f = t_0 I_{A^c B^c C^c} + t_1 I_{A^c B^c C} + t_2 I_{A^c B C^c} + t_3 I_{A^c B C} + t_4 I_{A B^c C^c}$$
$$+ t_5 I_{A B^c C} + t_6 I_{A B C^c} + t_7 I_{A B C}$$

Determine the numbers $t_0, t_1, \ldots t_7$ in terms of the numbers a, b, c. (See Prob. 2-13 for a general expression.)

2-13 Suppose a simple function f is given by

$$f = \sum_{i=0}^{N-1} a_i I_{A_i}$$

Let m_k be the kth minterm in the partition generated by the class $\{A_{N-1}, \ldots, A_0\}$. We may then write

$$f = \sum_{k=0}^{2^N-1} t_k I_{m_k}$$

The minterm number k is given by

$$k = \sum_{i=0}^{N-1} \beta_{ki} 2^i$$

where $\beta_{ki} = 0$ if A_i^c is in the kth minterm and $\beta_{ki} = 1$ if A_i is in the kth minterm. Show that

$$t_k = \sum_{i=0}^{N-1} \beta_{ki} a_i$$

2-14 Rearrange the variables in the minterm map of Fig. 2-7b so that the minterms are numbered sequentially in rows from left to right, with the minterm numbered 0 in its same position in the upper left-hand corner of the diagram.

2-15 Consider the partition generated by the sets A, B, C, D, E and represent the minterms on a map arranged as in Fig. 2-7b.

(**a**) Show that every product term, such as for example $B^c CDE^c$, obtained by suppressing the variable A from a minterm must give a pattern consisting of pairs of minterm blocks on the same row, separated by three minterm blocks.

(**b**) What is the pattern produced by suppressing the variable E from a minterm?

(**c**) What is the pattern produced by suppressing both A and E from a minterm?

2-16 A set of four cards is used to determine any integer from 0 through 15. Each card has eight numbers on the front, and each card is assigned a "value" or "weight." Cards A, B, C, and D have values 8, 4, 2, and 1, respectively. These may be used in a simple game as follows. A person is asked to pick a number. He is shown each card in turn and asked, "Is your number on this card?" The values of the cards for which the answer is "yes" are added to obtain the specified number.

    (a) Determine the numbers which should be on each of the cards; i.e., those which are examined before answering the question. (Suggestion: Use a minterm map.)

    (b) Suppose this game were extended to determine numbers— say the age of the subject—not exceeding 60. How many cards are needed and how many numbers are on each? How many if the numbers to be determined do not exceed 80?

2-17 Eighty students were questioned concerning their courses of study. The data obtained were:

There are 46 men, 18 of whom are engineering students.

There is 1 woman engineering student.

All engineering students take mathematics.

13 students take Latin, 2 of whom are engineers, 6 of whom are men.

25 men students and 5 women students take mathematics.

No women students and 3 men students take both Latin and mathematics.

    (a) How many students take neither mathematics nor Latin? How many of these are men?

    (b) How many men students take mathematics or Latin but not both?

Algebra of Set Operations and Switch- ing Algebra

Chapter 3

In Chap. 1, the fundamental set combinations known as union and intersection as well as the operation of taking complements were introduced. These operations are indicated by symbolic notation which makes possible succinct and precise statements of a complex sequence of such operations. In Chap. 2, the notion of a function was introduced and examined in some detail. In this chapter, we examine the symbolic representation of operations with sets in order to develop an *algebra of set operations*. This algebra is shown to be a very general form of those systems known as *Boolean algebras* (after the mathematician and logician George Boole, 1815–1864). By means of the indicator function introduced in Sec. 2-1, we develop a quasi-numerical form of the Boolean algebra which, because of its applications, is often referred to as *switching algebra*. The treatment set forth in this chapter has the advantage of relating switching algebra quite closely to the algebra of set operations (and hence to the algebra of events), in a manner that often facilitates the grasp of both operations and results.

3-1. An Algebra of Set Operations

Listed in Table 3-1 are a number of simple but important theorems which may be taken as the basis for an algebra of set operations. These theorems serve to define the rules of the algebra and to list some results which are useful for its extension. Several of these theorems have already been noted as set theorems, but they are reproduced here in a systematic listing which demonstrates important features of the algebra.

Set identities. Unless the special sets U and $\emptyset$ are designated or unless there are restrictive hypotheses, as for example in Theorems (VII) and (IX), the relations listed are true for any subsets of the universal set U. Thus the expressions are set identities—i.e., the statements do not depend upon the choice of sets.

Boolean Algebra. Although each of the theorems listed above may be obtained as a set theorem from the definitions by the use of the ordinary logic of mathematical reasoning, it is not necessary to develop all of them as set theorems. The first five pairs may be taken as basic, in the sense that the others may be derived directly from them as algebraic theorems, without reference to set theory. Since these first five pairs do not involve inclusion, one of the theorems on inclusion, say (IX), may be taken as the definition of inclusion. The other theorems on inclusion follow from this and the basic theorems. These results lead naturally to a consideration of the systems known as Boolean algebras.

An abstract Boolean algebra consists of a class of elements combinable under two binary operations, Boolean addition and Boolean multiplication, in accordance with certain postulated rules. The postulates may be given in a variety of forms; one commonly utilized form is due to the mathematician E. V. Huntington. For a careful treatment of abstract Boolean algebras, see Stabler [Ref. 13, pp. 193ff.] or Whitesitt [Ref. 15, chap. 2].

If the universal set U and its subsets, including the null set $\emptyset$, are considered as elements of the Boolean algebra; if set union is considered to be Boolean addition; and if set intersection is considered to be Boolean multiplication; then the first five pairs of set theorems in Table 3-1 show that Huntington's postulates are satisfied. The empty set $\emptyset$ plays the role of the identity element 0 with respect to

Table 3-1

$(I)\ A + B = B + A$	$(I')\ AB = BA$ — *(Commutative laws)*
$(II)\ A + (B + C) = (A + B) + C$ $A_n + \bigcup_{k \neq n} A_k = \bigcup_k A_k$	$(II')\ A(BC) = (AB)C$ — *(Associative laws)* $A_n\left(\bigcap_{k \neq n} A_k\right) = \bigcap_k A_k$
$(III)\ A + BC = (A + B)(A + C)$ $A + \bigcap_k B_k = \bigcap_k (A + B_k)$	$(III')\ A(B + C) = AB + AC$ — *(Distributive laws)* $A\left(\bigcup_k B_k\right) = \bigcup_k AB_k$
$(IV)\ A + \emptyset = A$	$(IV')\ AU = A$
$(V)\ A + A^c = U$	$(V')\ AA^c = \emptyset$
$(VI)\ (A^c)^c = A$	
$(VII)\ A = B$ iffi $A^c = B^c$	
$(VIII)\ (A + B)^c = A^c B^c$ $\left(\bigcup_k A_k\right)^c = \bigcap_k A_k^c$	$(VIII')\ (AB)^c = A^c + B^c$ — *(De Morgan's rules)* $\left(\bigcap_k A_k\right)^c = \bigcup_k A_k^c$
$(IX)\ A \subset B$ iffi $AB = A$	
$(X)\ A \subset B$ iffi $A^c + B = U$	$(X')\ A \supset B$ iffi $A^c B = \emptyset$
$(XI)\ A \subset B$ iffi $B^c \subset A^c$	
$(XII)\ \bigcup_{k=1}^{\infty} A_k = \bigcup_{k=1}^{\infty} B_k$, where $B_k = A_k \bigcap_{j=1}^{k-1} A_j^c$, so that $\{B_k\}$ is a disjoint class	

addition (set union) and the universal set U becomes the identity element 1 with respect to multiplication (set intersection).

All the results of Boolean algebra may be transferred to the algebra of set operations. In Refs. 13 and 15, for example, Theorems (VI), (VII), (VIII), and $(VIII')$ are shown to be consequences of the first five pairs. The set Theorem (IX) may be used as a definition of inclusion in abstract algebra, and the other theorems on inclusion derived therefrom.

The system of postulates is not unique. Some of the statements listed as theorems from the first five pairs could be substituted for appropriate statements among the first five pairs. The latter could then be derived as theorems. Any suitable set of postulates, however, would make it possible to derive the remaining members of the first five pairs not included in the list of postulates.

The relationship between the algebra of set operations and abstract Boolean algebra is closer than is apparent from the foregoing discussion. The mathematician M. H. Stone has shown that every abstract algebra is essentially equivalent to (isomorphic to) an algebra of set operations. It should be noted that the algebra of set operations is to be distinguished from a quite different concept known variously as an algebra of sets, a field of sets, or an additive class of sets. The latter concept, useful in the theory of measure and probability, is discussed briefly in Chap. 5. On occasion, we shall shorten the expression "algebra of set operations" to "algebra of sets" in the interest of style and when the context makes the usage clear.

Although we shall take the algebra of set operations as basic for the purposes of this study, the recognition that an algebra of sets is a Boolean algebra has important advantages. We may approach a problem of set relationships such as may arise in a problem in switching circuits in more than one manner. If a result can be obtained and visualized more easily as a set theorem, then it should be so obtained. If utilization of the formal procedures of Boolean algebra is the more expedient, then that course is open to us.

As an example, we may consider Theorem (XII), which is included in the list because of its usefulness in probability theory. It may be approached as a set theorem. Because of (II') and (V'), we may assert that $B_n B_m = \emptyset$ whenever $n \neq m$, so that the B_k form a disjoint class. For simplicity, call the union of all the A_k the set A and the union of all the B_k the set B. Suppose x is any element in A; it is then in A_n for some n. Let N be the smallest such n. Then

$$x \in \bigcup_{k=1}^{N} A_k \quad \text{but} \quad x \notin \bigcup_{k=1}^{N-1} A_k$$

so that by (VIII)

$$x \in \bigcap_{k=1}^{N-1} A_k{}^c$$

Thus, x must be a member of B_N and hence of B. On the other hand, if x belongs to B, it belongs to B_n for some choice of n and hence to A_n for this choice of n. The element x must therefore be a member of A. Because of the arbitrariness of the element x in the argument, we have verified that $A \subset B$ and $B \subset A$, which by definition ensures equality.

The theorem could be proved from the theorems listed above it in Table 3-1 without resorting to set ideas. It appears in this case that the argument would be more involved than the simple, straightforward one obtained from the set interpretation of the algebraic expressions. Thus, in this case it is expedient to use the set approach.

Duality. Several of the statements in Table 3-1 are paired by writing them in parallel columns and giving them similar numbers. The pairings exhibit an important duality. In each case, one statement may be derived from another by interchanging each of the following: (1) intersection and union, (2) U and $\emptyset$, and (3) $\subset$ and $\supset$.

The nature of this duality can perhaps be made clear by means of simple examples. Consider first the set identity

$$(A + B)C = AC + BC$$

If every union is replaced by an intersection and conversely, the result is the expression

$$AB + C = (A + C)(B + C)$$

which is also a set identity. The fact that the second identity follows from the first may be shown as follows. Utilizing Theorem (VII), we may take complements of both sides of the first equation. According to De Morgan's rules, there results

$$A^c B^c + C^c = (A^c + C^c)(B^c + C^c)$$

Even if the first statement above were only an equality depending upon the particular choice of sets A, B, and C, the latter statement would follow. Since, however, the first statement is a set identity, it holds if each set is replaced by its complement. In this case, the third equation takes on the same form as the second.

An example involving the relation of inclusion is the following:

$$(A + B)(A + D) \subset B(A + D) + (A + B)$$

Since this is a set identity, use of the duality principle leads immediately to the assertion

$$AB + AD \supset (B + AD)(AB)$$

Use of De Morgan's rule and Theorem (XI) leads from the first expression to the expression

$$A^c B^c + A^c D^c \supset (B^c + A^c D^c)(A^c B^c)$$

Removal of the complement signs is permissible in general only when the first expression is a set identity. De Morgan's rule and the pattern of duality noted above leads to the important principle of duality.

Principle of Duality. Any valid relationship holding among sets obtained by forming unions, intersections, and complements is transformed into a new valid relationship by complementing the various sets and by interchanging each of the following: (1) intersection and union, (2) U and $\emptyset$, and (3) $\subset$ and $\supset$. If the original expression is one holding identically among sets, the complementing of the sets in the original expression need not be made.

3-2. *The Indicator Function and Set Operations*

The indicator function defined in Sec. 2-1 is extremely useful in dealing with set relations and operations. We list below several important properties of indicator functions and then show two important ways they may be used in dealing with set operations. For brevity, we drop the argument x and simply indicate the function. The following theorems are proved in a direct manner from the definitions.

(I1) $I_A \leq I_B$ iffi $A \subset B$

(I2) $I_A \equiv I_B$ iffi $A = B$

(I3) $I_A \equiv 0$ iffi $A = \emptyset$

(I4) $I_A \equiv 1$ iffi $A = U$

(I5) $I_{AB} \equiv I_A I_B \equiv \min(I_A, I_B)$

(I6) $I_{A+B} \equiv I_A + I_B - I_{AB} \equiv \max (I_A, I_B)$

(I7) $I_{A^c} \equiv 1 - I_A$

(I8) $I_{AB^c} \equiv I_A - I_{AB}$

(I9) $\{x: I_A \neq I_B\} = A \oplus B$

As an example, we consider a proof of (I5). We note that each element x must be in one of the minterms of the partition generated by sets A and B. If an element is in AB, then $I_A = 1$, $I_B = 1$, and $I_{AB} = 1$, so that the theorem is satisfied. If the element is in any of the other cells, $I_{AB} = 0$ and at least one of the functions I_A and I_B is 0, which completes the proof.

It should be noted that addition and multiplication signs are used in two different ways in the theorems. In the expression I_{A+B}, the plus sign indicates set union. In the expression $I_A + I_B - I_{AB}$, the plus sign indicates ordinary addition of numbers and the minus sign indicates ordinary subtraction. It was noted in Chap. 1 that the minus sign, when used to indicate a set relationship, has a meaning quite different from that of ordinary subtraction. In the expression $I_A I_B$, ordinary multiplication of numbers is indicated.

The proof of (I5) utilizes a simple case of an important principle which we wish to generalize. We consider the partition generated by the sets $A_0, A_1, \ldots, A_N$. Suppose F is a set obtained by taking unions, intersections, and complements of the generating sets A_k. We may then assert the following general theorem:

(I10) The indicator function I_F for the combination F of the generating sets is constant over each of the 2^{N+1} minterms in the partition generated by $A_0, A_1, \ldots, A_N$.

This theorem implies that to evaluate and hence define I_F it is sufficient to evaluate it for one element in each of the 2^{N+1} minterms.

To see the validity of this theorem, we note that (1) the value of I_{A_k}, for any $k = 0, 1, \ldots, N$ is constant over any given minterm, for within that minterm every element is in one and only one of the sets A_k or A_k^c; (2) the value of the indicator function I_F is a function of the values of the indicator functions for the component sets, none of which change in value over any given minterm.

The theorems above may be utilized to give simple arithmetic proofs of many set theorems. This can be illustrated by the following examples.

To prove the set theorem (XI), we note that $I_A \leq I_B$ iffi $1 - I_B \leq 1 - I_A$. By Theorem $(I7)$, this is equivalent to $I_{B^c} \leq I_{A^c}$. Use of Theorem $(I1)$ completes the proof.

The fact that $(A + B)C = AC + BC$ may be demonstrated by the following manipulations:

$$I_{(A+B)C} = I_{A+B}I_C = (I_A + I_B - I_{AB})I_C = I_AI_C + I_BI_C - I_{AB}I_C$$
$$= I_{AC} + I_{BC} - I_AI_BI_CI_C = I_{AC} + I_{BC} - I_{ACBC}$$
$$= I_{AC+BC}$$

Each step is justified by one or more of the theorems on indicator functions. Theorem $(I2)$ serves to complete the proof.

A second procedure utilizes systematically Theorem $(I10)$, above. We may illustrate this method by demonstrating again that

$$(A + B)C = AC + BC$$

We wish to show that $I_{(A+B)C} = I_{AC+BC}$. To do this, we evaluate the indicator functions on the eight minterms determined by the sets A, B, and C, and compare the resulting values. The procedure is outlined in Table 3-2. For each of the eight minterms, the values of I_A, I_B, and

Table 3-2

Minterms	I_A	I_B	I_C	I_{A+B}	$I_{(A+B)C}$	I_{AC}	I_{BC}	I_{AC+BC}
$A^cB^cC^c$	0	0	0	0	0	0	0	0
A^cB^cC	0	0	1	0	0	0	0	0
$A^cB\ C^c$	0	1	0	1	0	0	0	0
$A^cB\ C$	0	1	1	1	1	0	1	1
$A\ B^cC^c$	1	0	0	1	0	0	0	0
$A\ B^cC$	1	0	1	1	1	1	0	1
$A\ B\ C^c$	1	1	0	1	0	0	0	0
$A\ B\ C$	1	1	1	1	1	1	1	1

I_C are determined. This is done simply by noting whether the minterm in question has A or A^c, B or B^c, and C or C^c as a factor and giving the indicator functions the appropriate values. Step-by-step use of properties of the indicator functions makes it possible to calculate values of the indicators for various set combinations until the desired combinations are obtained.   Comparison of the values of the indicator functions $I_{(A+B)C}$ and I_{AC+BC} on the eight minterms demonstrates their identity and hence the equality of the sets.

The evaluations may be carried out most efficiently by using the forms $I_{AB} = \min (I_A, I_B)$ and $I_{A+B} = \max (I_A, I_B)$.   Comparison of the values for the two functions under consideration may be carried out by noting that all the 1s in the two columns match up.   If there were fewer 0s than 1s, the 0s could be matched.

An alternative form of the set expressions may be derived from the information in Table 3-2.   A given minterm occurs iffi I_A, I_B, and I_C have the combination of values shown in that row in the table.   This means that the indicator function for the minterm has the value 1 iffi I_A, I_B, and I_C have the specified combination of values.   Consider the values for the function I_{AC+BC}.   It is apparent that

$$I_{A^cBC} + I_{AB^cC} + I_{ABC} = I_{AC+BC}$$

so that we must have

$$A^cBC + AB^cC + ABC = AC + BC = (A + B)C$$

It should be apparent that the process is quite general.   *Any of the set expressions may be written as a sum of appropriate minterms.*   These minterms are those for which the indicator function for the set expression has the value 1.

3-3. *Numerical Form of the Algebra*

A very useful numerical interpretation of the algebra may be made with the aid of the indicator function.   The resulting numerical manipulations are those which are usually presented in engineering treatments of Boolean algebra for switching or logic networks.   We may proceed in the following way.   For any choice of sets A, B, C, etc., we may replace

$$I_{A+B} \text{ by } A + B \qquad I_{AB} \text{ by } AB \qquad I_{A^c} \text{ by } A^c$$

and suppose the symbols to have possible numerical values 0 or 1. Now

(i) $I_{A+B} = 1$ iffi $I_A = 1$ or $I_B = 1$ or both
(ii) $I_{AB} = 1$ iffi $I_A = I_B = 1$
(iii) $I_{A^c} = 1$ iffi $I_A = 0$

These relations are summarized in the following table.

(i) Addition	(ii) Multiplication	(iii) Negation
$0 + 0 = 0$	$0 \cdot 0 = 0$	$0^c = 1$
$0 + 1 = 1$	$0 \cdot 1 = 0$	$1^c = 0$
$1 + 0 = 1$	$1 \cdot 0 = 0$	
$1 + 1 = 1$	$1 \cdot 1 = 1$	

Since $I_U \equiv 1$ and $I_\emptyset \equiv 0$, it is convenient to replace U by 1 and $\emptyset$ by 0 whenever they appear in an expression. The following rules are consistent with the above tables.

(i) $A + 1 = 1 + A = 1$ (ii) $A1 = 1A = A$
    $A + 0 = 0 + A = A$ $A0 = 0A = 0$

It should be noted that the symbols $A, B, C, \ldots$ are being used in two entirely different ways. Viewed one way, they represent sets or events. On the numerical interpretation, they are symbols to represent values of the indicator functions $I_A, I_B, I_C, \ldots$. It is important to keep in mind the distinction, but a little care will prevent confusion. The representation has the value that either interpretation may be used. It is sometimes convenient to use one or the other or both alternately in thinking about a particular problem.

In dealing with events, we are usually concerned with the question: "Has the event occurred?" In the new terminology, the statement "the event A has occurred" is equivalent to the assertion "$A = 1$." This is not an identity, but a statement that in the case under consideration A has the value 1.

Consider again the logic networks dealt with in Sec. 1-6. The statement "the event A has occurred" is, for these networks, equivalent to the statement "$E_a = E$," which in turn is equivalent to the numerical condition $A = 1$. For the various elementary networks considered in Sec. 1-6, we may replace the matrix of states with the *logic matrix*, as is shown in Figs. 3-1 to 3-3. It is also customary to indicate the terminals $a, b, c, \ldots$ by the letters $A, B, C, \ldots$, respectively. This is actually a third use of the letters $A, B, C, \ldots$, but it is a perfectly natural one. The single symbol thus indicates the event, the terminal whose voltage determines the event, and the numerical value of the indicator function for the event. Since the relationship between the driving variables and the output variable is expressible in a set relationship, it is often convenient to designate the output terminal with the appropriate algebraic expression. For example, the output of the OR circuit may be designated $A + B$.

Table 3-2 was derived as a table of values of the indicator function when the elementary event belongs to one of the characteristic events designated by the appropriate minterm. This table is converted to a logic matrix simply by changing the column headings to the symbols

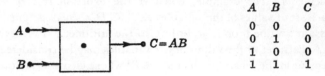

A	B	C
0	0	0
0	1	0
1	0	0
1	1	1

Fig. 3-1 The AND circuit and its logic matrix.

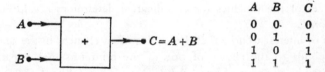

A	B	C
0	0	0
0	1	1
1	0	1
1	1	1

Fig. 3-2 The OR circuit and its logic matrix.

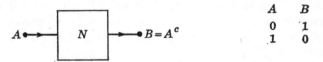

A	B
0	1
1	0

Fig. 3-3 The NOT circuit and its logic matrix.

corresponding to the sets. The numerical interpretation of the algebra is employed.

The numerical valued algebra just introduced is often referred to as *switching algebra* because of the application to switching circuits. It could have been introduced simply as an abstract Boolean algebra having only two elements, 0 and 1. The treatment adopted above has the advantage of tying switching algebra to the concept of sets and the corresponding idea of events in a useful manner.

Duality. It should be apparent that the principle of duality extends to the numerical form of the algebra, so that one functional identity may be transformed into another by the use of this principle.

3-4. Boolean Functions

With the introduction of the numerical interpretation of the Boolean algebra, i.e., the switching algebra, it is natural to introduce the idea of a *Boolean function*. Consider any expression derived from a set of Boolean variables A, B, C, D by the operations of taking sums, products, and complements. For example, consider the expression $A(B^c + CD)$. For each set of values of the variables A, B, C, D, there is assigned to the expression a value 0 or 1, according to the arithmetic laws developed above. Each set of the values of the variables may be considered to be an element in the binary product space B^4 whose elements are the four-tuples of numbers (A,B,C,D), where each of these coordinates has the value 0 or 1. The functional expression thus defines a function whose domain is B^4 and whose range T is the set $\{0,1\}$. Each choice of a set of values of the variables (or coordinates) determines a value of the function F.

It is of interest to note that the choice of an element in the space B^4 corresponds to the choice of one of the minterms in the partition generated by the class of sets $\{A,B,C,D\}$. In fact, the set of 0s and 1s designating the element in B^4 may be considered to be the binary expression of the minterm number determined according to the scheme developed in connection with minterm maps in Sec. 2-5. It is also apparent that the binary space B^4 is precisely the binary product space corresponding to the partition generated by the class $\{A,B,C,D\}$, as described in Sec. 2-4.

From a set-theoretic point of view, the expression describing the function is a set obtained by forming unions, intersections, and complements of members and of permissible combinations of members of the class $\{A,B,C,D\}$. We may refer to this as the *function set* for the function. Examination of the laws of calculation used in determining functional values shows that from a set point of view the *Boolean function is precisely the indicator function for the function set.*

In the case of three variables A, B, C, we may illustrate by use of the functions in Table 3-2. When converted to a logic matrix, this table has a complete tabulation of the values of the Boolean functions given by the expressions

$$f_1(A,B,C) = A + B \qquad f_4(A,B,C) = BC$$
$$f_2(A,B,C) = (A + B)C \qquad f_5(A,B,C) = AC + BC$$
$$f_3(A,B,C) = AC$$

The expressions are all considered to be functions of the three variables A, B, C. Where one of the variables is absent in the describing expression for the function, the value of the function is independent of the value of that variable. The functional descriptions in the table are complete. The sets of variable values which make each of the minterms equal 1, in turn, exhaust all the possible sets of values. Thus, the table shows that $f_2(A,B,C) = f_5(A,B,C)$. In set terms, this means that we have set equality; that is, $(A + B)C = AC + BC$. The values of the functions f_2 and f_5 are the values of the corresponding indicator functions for the function sets. In this case, of course, they are identical.

A pair of theorems which we shall refer to as *Boole's expansion theorems* have been found useful in numerous applications. These may be stated as follows:

$$f(A,B,C, \ldots) = Af(1,B,C, \ldots) + A^c f(0,B,C, \ldots) \qquad \text{(I)}$$
$$f(A,B,C, \ldots) = [A^c + f(1,B,C, \ldots)][A + f(0,B,C, \ldots)] \qquad \text{(II)}$$

The theorems can be proved by noting that under the two conditions $A = 1$ and $A = 0$ the expressions reduce to identities. It should be apparent that the expansion could have been used for any variable; the choice of A in the expressions above is arbitrary, and the same argument could be carried out for any of the variables. As a simple example to illustrate the use of the first expansion theorem, we may write

$$(A + B)C^c + AD = A[C^c + D] + A^c[BC^c]$$

Use of the square brackets in the right-hand member is for the purpose of identifying the factors corresponding to those in the general expression. In a similar manner we may utilize the second expansion to write

$$(A + B)C^c + AD = [A^c + C^c + D][A + BC^c]$$

3-5. Representation of Boolean Functions

The usefulness of the Boolean algebra rests in part on the facility with which Boolean functions may be manipulated into different forms and with which Boolean functions in various forms may be compared. To this end, a variety of representations have been employed. In this section we summarize several of these. Some of the material of this section is a restatement or an easy extension of results of previous sections.

Logic Matrices. The logic matrix as a development of the matrix of states has been introduced in Secs. 3-2 and 3-3 as a means of representing Boolean functions of several variables. That development indicates various helpful ways of viewing the information contained in the logic matrix. This previous development has indicated that a Boolean function of N variables has the following characteristics:

1. It has 2^N minterms, which are the cells for the partition generated by the N sets. A given combination of values for the N variables makes one and only one of the minterms have the value 1.

Table 3-3

No.	A	B	C	Minterms	Values (example)
0	0	0	0	$m_0 = A^c B^c C^c$	$F_0 = 1$
1	0	0	1	$m_1 = A^c B^c C$	$F_1 = 0$
2	0	1	0	$m_2 = A^c B\ C^c$	$F_2 = 1$
3	0	1	1	$m_3 = A^c B\ C$	$F_3 = 0$
4	1	0	0	$m_4 = A\ B^c C^c$	$F_4 = 1$
5	1	0	1	$m_5 = A\ B^c C$	$F_5 = 0$
6	1	1	0	$m_6 = A\ B\ C^c$	$F_6 = 0$
7	1	1	1	$m_7 = A\ B\ C$	$F_7 = 1$

2. It has 2^N functional values, one for each minterm. Determination of this set of functional values completely determines the Boolean function. There are 2^P Boolean functions of N variables, where $P = 2^N$, provided the trivial cases of the function identically 0 and the function identically 1 are counted.

3. It can always be expressed as the Boolean sum of those minterms for which the function has the value 1. This sum of minterms is often known as the *first canonical form*.

A Boolean function may be expressed completely by its logic matrix. Table 3-3 shows the general situation for $N = 3$. The minterms are arranged systematically according to the sets of values of the variables A, B, C which make them take on the value 1. The arrangement of the 0s and 1s is such that the set of 0s and 1s forms the binary number representation of the place in the table (starting with 0). The decimal equivalents of these binary numbers are shown in the first column. It is convenient to indicate the various minterms by m_0, m_1, . . . , m_7. A given minterm is readily determined from this notation. For example, consider m_3. The binary equivalent of 3 is 011. The corresponding minterm has the value 1 when $A = 0$, $B = 1$, and $C = 1$. This must be the minterm A^cBC.

The numerical example whose values are shown in the values column is the Boolean function

$$F = f(A,B,C) = (AB)^cC^c + ABC$$

It is readily seen that $F = 1$ if $ABC = 1$. Examination of the first term shows that $F = 1$ provided $C = 0$ and A and B do not both have the value 1. This occurs for minterms numbered 0, 2, and 4. The function can therefore be put in the canonical form

$$F = m_0 + m_2 + m_4 + m_7 = A^cB^cC^c + A^cBC^c + AB^cC^c + ABC$$

Algebraic manipulations serve to put this function into other forms. For example,

$$F = A^cC^c + A(B^cC^c + BC) = A^cC^c + B^cC^c + ABC$$

Sigma Form. The pertinent information for describing a particular function represented according to the scheme in Table 3-3 is the numbers of the minterms in the canonical form. A compact notation for representing the function which is finding some popularity in the literature is the following:

$$F = \Sigma(0,2,4,7)$$

The sigma or summation sign serves to denote the Boolean summation of the minterms whose numbers are given. To use this notation it is necessary to know the order in which the variables are to be arranged in the minterms.

Related Forms. For certain theoretical purposes, it is sometimes convenient to express the function as a sum in a manner essentially equivalent to the first canonical form as follows:

$$F = \sum_{k=0}^{2^N-1} F_k m_k$$

where m_k is the kth minterm and F_k is the value of the function on the kth minterm.   The relation of this notation to the display of functional values in Table 3-3 (where $N = 3$) should be apparent.   The expression may be viewed either as the functional description in terms of the numerical valued variables or as a set expression, provided m_k is understood to indicate the kth minterm (viewed as a set) and the functional values F_k are interpreted in terms of the empty set $\emptyset$ and the universal set U, corresponding to the values 0 and 1, respectively.

An alternative way of indicating the summation has also been found useful for certain theoretical purposes.   If we let J_F be the *index set* for the function, in the sense that it contains those k for which $F_k = 1$, we may then write

$$F = \sum_{k \in J_F} m_k$$

This notation emphasizes the fact that the function is determined uniquely by the index set for the Boolean function (provided the number and order of variables is known).   For the function in Table 3-3, the index set J_F is the set 0, 2, 4, 7.   These are just the minterm numbers listed in the sigma form, above.

The point function on the universal set corresponding to the Boolean function may be written

$$I_F(x) = \sum_{k=0}^{2^N - 1} F_k I_{m_k}(x) = \sum_{k \in J_F} I_{m_k}(x)$$

where F_k is interpreted as an ordinary number, 0 or 1.

Minterm Maps.   An alternative to the tabular form of the logic matrix of the type shown in Table 3-3 is provided by the minterm maps of Sec. 2-5 (see Figs. 2-6 and 2-7).   It is pointed out in the discussion of Sec. 2-5 that the minterms are arranged systematically according to the numbering system adopted for Tables 3-2 and 3-3.   A Boolean function can be represented unambiguously by putting a 1, or other identifying mark, in each minterm area for which the function has the value 1.   The function given in Table 3-3 is shown on the minterm map of Fig. 3-4.

Alternative forms of the Boolean function may be recognized from the minterm map.   The part of the map that is made up of the minterm blocks 0 and 2 may be recognized as representing $A^c C^c$, for this part of the map fails to be in A and at the same time fails to be in C. The part of the map which represents $B^cC^c + BC$ is recognized to consist of the minterm blocks 0, 4, 3, 7. Of these, only 4 and 7 are also in A. Thus the function represented may be expressed $A(B^cC^c + BC) + A^cC^c$. Other forms of the function are similarly recognizable. It should be noted that in deriving various forms the same minterm may appear in several terms of a Boolean sum. Systematic exploitation of certain patterns of block arrangements may be used for rapid manipulation of functional forms [Ref. 3, 8, or 11].

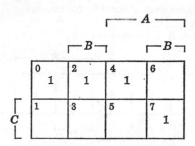

Fig. 3-4 Minterm map representation of the Boolean function of Table 3-1.

Function Designation Number. The treatment of Boolean functions has resulted in a systematic numbering of the minterms m_k, with k running from $k = 0$ to $k = 2^N - 1$ in the case of N variables. A corresponding numbering of functions is also feasible [8]. A Boolean function is determined by finding the functional value F_k on each of these minterms. This is illustrated in Table 3-3 for a function of three variables. In the case of three variables, suppose the functional values are arranged systematically $F_7, F_6, \ldots, F_0$. The result is an ordered sequence of eight numbers, each of which is either 0 or 1. Thus, for the function in Table 3-3 this sequence is 10010101. This sequence may be considered to be a binary number. Its decimal equivalent is 149. This number, written in binary form in eight places, uniquely characterizes the function. It is convenient to call this number the *function designation number* n_F for the function F. Alternative equivalent terms are the *function designator* and the *function number*. In cases where n_F is expressed in binary form, it may be convenient to refer to the *binary designator*. It is only necessary to know the number of variables

N, the order in which they are handled, and the function number n_F in order to determine uniquely any Boolean function. The binary designator may be considered as a special minterm map in which all the minterms are arranged sequentially in a row with m_0 on the right, as is illustrated for three variables in Fig. 3-5.

Values of n_F for functions of N variables run from $n_F = 0$ to $n_F = 2^P - 1$, where $P = 2^N$. The function numbered 0 according to this scheme is the function which is identically 0 and the one numbered $2^P - 1$ is the function which is identically 1. For theoretical purposes it is sometimes desirable to express n_F in a form closely

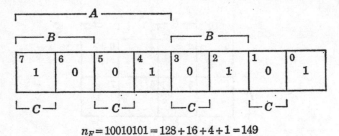

$$n_F = 10010101 = 128 + 16 + 4 + 1 = 149$$

Fig. 3-5   Special form of the minterm map for three variables to display the function number in binary form (i.e., the binary designator).

related to the summation forms discussed earlier in this section. We have the formulas

$$n_F = \sum_{k=0}^{2^N-1} F_k 2^k = \sum_{k \in J_F} 2^k$$

where F_k is the kth functional value and J_F is the index set for the function, as defined above.

Operations directly analogous to those carried out in Table 3-2 to determine the functional values for various expressions can be carried out systematically and compactly in terms of the binary designator. Suppose there are N variables, A_{N-1}, A_{N-2}, . . . , A_0. The function numbers in binary form will have 2^N places, which for convenience may be blocked off in groups of four. The basic function A_k has a binary designator which consists of alternate packets of 2^k 1s and 0s, starting with 1s at the left. Function designators for sums and products of functions may be obtained by applying the maximum and minimum rules for sums and products to the individual places (corresponding to minterms) in the binary designators. The operations in Table 3-2 may be presented in these terms as follows:

Function	Binary designator
A,B,C	7654 3210*
A	1111 0000
B	1100 1100
C	1010 1010
$A + B$	1111 1100
$(A + B)C$	$1010\ 1000 = 128 + 32 + 8 = 168$
AC	1010 0000
BC	1000 1000
$AC + BC$	$1010\ 1000 = 168$

* Place numbers, corresponding to minterm numbers.

There are no complements in the operations above. To obtain the binary designator for the complement of a function, simply take the 1s complement of the binary designator for the original function. Thus, in the table above, $A + B$ has the binary designator 1111 1100. The binary designator for $(A + B)^c$ is 0000 0011, which is obtained by interchanging each 0 for a 1 and each 1 for a 0.

3-6. Null Minterms and Optional Minterms

Previous discussions of minterms and the representation of functions as sums (unions) of minterms has proceeded as if each minterm were nonempty (i.e., as if the event represented could occur). Nothing is lost, however, when the choice of generating sets is such that some of the minterms are empty. It sometimes occurs in applications of switching algebra that physical constraints on the system represented ensure that some of the minterms cannot occur. In this case, it is often possible to exploit the constraining conditions in the design of switching networks. In other situations, the occurrence of certain minterms may not be inhibited, but the occurrence or nonoccurrence does not affect the behavior of the system. In either case, two functions are effectively equivalent iffi they agree on the nonnull or nonoptional minterms. Functional inequalities may also be handled in terms of the effective minterms.

We may illustrate these facts by simple examples.   Consider two sets A and B as functions of the pair of variables A, B.   We use the binary designators.

$$
\begin{array}{ll}
A,B & 3210 \\
A & 1100 \\
B & 1010
\end{array}
$$

It is apparent that $A \subset B$ iffi $m_2 = \emptyset$.   But $m_2 = AB^c$, so that we have the result $A \subset B$ iffi $AB^c = \emptyset$.   Or at least the inequality holds effectively if the occurrence or nonoccurrence of AB^c is of no consequence.

As a second example, consider the function $A(B^c + C) + A^cB$ under the condition that $m_6 = ABC^c = \emptyset$.   We write the table with the sign $\emptyset$ in the m_6 column.

$$
\begin{array}{ll}
A,B,C & 7654\ 3210 \\
A & 1\emptyset11\ 0000 \\
B & 1\emptyset00\ 1100 \\
C & 1\emptyset10\ 1010 \\
A(B^c + C) + A^cB & 1\emptyset11\ 1100 \\
A + B & 1\emptyset11\ 1100
\end{array}
$$

Examination shows that under the constraint, the designator for the function $A + B$ is $1\emptyset11\ 1100$, so that under the constraint the original function is indistinguishable from the simpler function $A + B$. Systematic exploitation of such constraints is common in the design of switching or logic networks.

Problems

3-1 Verify the following relationships (1) algebraically, using theorems of Table 3-1; (2) using properties of indicator functions of Sec. 3-2; and (3) using minterm maps.

(a) Take as definition $A \oplus B = AB^c + A^cB$.   Show that
$A \oplus B = (A + B)(AB)^c = (A^c \oplus B)^c = (A \oplus B^c)^c$.

(b) $A = A + AB = A(A + B)$

(c) $A + A^cB = A + B$

(d) $AC + A^cB + BC = (A + B)(A^c + C) = AC + A^cB$

(e) $AB^c + BC^c + B^cC + A^cB = AB^c + BC^c + A^cC$
$\qquad\qquad\qquad\qquad = AC^c + B^cC + A^cB$

(f) $AB + AC^c + A^cC + A^cB^cD^c$
$\qquad\qquad\qquad = (A^c + B + C^c)(A + C + B^cD^c)$

(g) $AB(C + D^cE) \subset B[(A^c + B^c + D + E^c)C^c]^c$

 (h) $(AD^c + A^c)B^c + D[A(B^c + C^c)]^c$
$$= A^c(B^c + D) + AB^cD^c + BCD$$
 (i) $AB + C + (AB + C)^c(CB + A) = A + C$
 (j) $(A + B)(AD)^cC = A^cBC + ACD^c$

3-2 Use properties of indicator functions given in Sec. 3-2 to establish the following:

 (a) If $A \subset B$, $I_{AB} = I_A$.
 (b) If $A \subset B$, $I_B - I_A = I_{BA^c}$.
 (c) If $\{A_i\}$ is a disjoint class whose union is A, then $I_A = \Sigma I_{A_i}$.

3-3 Verify the relations listed below: (1) by the use of logic matrices; (2) by the use of minterm maps.

 (a) $AC + A^cB + BC = AC + A^cB$
 (b) $AB^c + BC^c + B^cC + A^cB = AB^c + BC^c + A^cC$
$$= AC^c + B^cC + A^cB$$
 (c) $AB^c + BC^cD + A^cCD \subset AC^c + AB^cC + A^cD$
 (d) $A^c(B + C^c)^c + C[A(B^c + D) + AB + B^cD^c] = (A + B^c)^c$

3-4 In the following problem, assume that the functions considered are all functions of the five Boolean variables A, B, C, D, E, taken in that order. Thus, there are 32 *minterms*, $m_0, m_1, \ldots, m_{31}$. A *maxterm* M_k is the Boolean sum of five Boolean variables, the first being either A or A^c, the second being B or B^c, etc. For example, $M_3 = A^c + B^c + C^c + D + E$. Note that maxterms as well as minterms are numbered according to the scheme used in Table 3-3 of the text.

 (a) Express the maxterm M_3 as a sum of minterms.
 (b) Show that $m_k{}^c = M_{31-k}$. Use the fact that the binary number obtained by interchanging 0s and 1s in five places is $31 - k$, when the original number is k. A properly handled example exhibiting the essential pattern of a general proof is sufficient.
 (c) It is apparent from the pattern developed in the text that a Boolean function may be expressed in the *first canonical form* as

$$F(A,B,C,D,E) = \sum_{k=0}^{31} F_k m_k \tag{1}$$

with the set of functional values F_k determining the function completely.   Show that

$$F(A,B,C,D,E) = \prod_{k=0}^{31} (M_{31-k} + F_k) \qquad (2)$$

The symbol Π indicates the Boolean product.   Note that since $A + 1 = 1$, the only factors other than unity are those for which $F_k = 0$.   The form (2) is often referred to as the *second canonical form*.

(d) Express the function

$$F = C^cD^cE^c + CDE + A^cB^cD + ABCD + BCE + AB^cC^cE$$

in both form (1) and form (2).

3-5 For each Boolean function F listed below, write the first canonical form; write the first canonical form for the complementary function F^c; and use De Morgan's rules to obtain the second canonical form [form (2) of Prob. 3-4].

   (a) $F(A,B,C) = AB^c + B(A + C^c)$
   (b) $F(A,B,C,D) = (A + D^c)(B^c + C)^c + ABD$

3-6 For each Boolean function listed below: (1) write the logic matrix; (2) represent on a minterm map; (3) write the first canonical form; (4) write the second canonical form (see Probs. 3-4 and 3-5); and (5) determine the function designator n_F in binary form and convert it to the decimal equivalent.

   (a) $F(A,B,C,D) = (A^c + B + C^c)(A + C + B^cD^c)$
   (b) $F(A,B,C,D) = C^cD^c + ABD^c + A^cBC^c + A^cB^cCD^c$
   $$\qquad\qquad\qquad\qquad\qquad + AB^cC^cD + B^cCD$$
   (c) $F(A,B,C,D) = AB^c + CD^c + DA^c$

3-7 **(a)** Show that $(A \oplus B) \oplus C = A \oplus (B \oplus C)$, so that it is meaningful to speak of $A \oplus B \oplus C$.   (Suggestion: Use the form $A \oplus B = AB^c + A^cB$ and express the functions in first canonical form.)

   (b) Draw a Venn diagram or a minterm map and illustrate the fact that $A \oplus B \oplus C$ is the part of the diagram that is in an *odd number* of the sets A, B, and C.

(c) Generalize, by an inductive proof, the result of part (b) to the disjunctive union of an arbitrary number N of sets. (Suggestion: Use the fact that the complement of a function which is the union of those minterms with an odd number of uncomplemented factors is the function which is the union of those minterms with an even number of uncomplemented factors.)

3-8 For the expressions listed below: (1) check the validity of the expressions when all minterms are considered important; (2) check the validity of the expressions when the minterms so designated are optional or impossible (empty).

(a) $AB + (C + D^c)^c + (E + BD)^c \subset A(B + C^cD)$
$$+ E^c(B^c + D^c) \qquad A^cC^cD = \emptyset$$
(b) $A^cC + A(C^c + B) = A + C \qquad AC = \emptyset$

3-9 For the expressions below, tell what minterms must be optional or impossible in order for the expressions to be valid:

(a) $B(A + C^cD) + C(A^cD + AB^c) + AB^cD = A + D$
(b) $A + BD = D + ACD^c$

3-10 Show that $B = C$ iffi both $AB = AC$ and $A + B = A + C$. Give two proofs:

(a) Using indicator functions
(b) Using an argument based on null minterms in the partition generated by A, B, C

Boolean Functions and Logic Networks

Chapter 4

The ideas developed in preceding chapters have been applied extensively by engineers to the analysis and design of various types of switching or logic networks. There are two aspects of the design of such systems: the *circuit design* aspect, which seeks to make economical and reliable elements operate in the desired manner; and the *logical design* aspect, which seeks to discover the most economical and reliable switching systems to provide the desired system behavior. Attention is focused in this work on the switching or logical aspect, with practically no attention to the problem of making circuit components behave in reasonable approximation to the simple switching behavior assumed for logical analysis. For treatments of both the circuit design aspect as well as more detailed consideration of logical design, one may consult Refs. 3, 8, 11, and to some extent 15. These deal extensively with logical design and may serve as guides to the large and growing literature in the field.

4-1. *Some Applications to Logic Networks*

In Sec. 1-6, the AND, OR, and NOT logic elements are described in terms of the terminal states. In Sec. 3-5, this description is made in terms of the logic matrix. We turn now to the problem of realizing more complicated set combinations or Boolean functions by combining these basic units. Before doing so, however, it may be of interest to consider one practical form of circuit realization of these basic units. For the AND and OR circuits, we may use as a basic circuit element the diode rectifier, which is characterized by low resistance to currents in the "forward" direction and by high resistance to currents in the "backward" direction.

The OR circuit of Fig. 4-1 may be understood by noting that E_d is approximately equal to the minimum of the voltages E_a, E_b, and E_c.

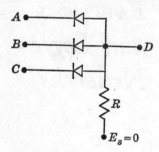

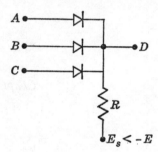

Fig. 4-1 A diode OR circuit.

Fig. 4-2 A diode AND circuit.

We suppose that each of the latter voltages is allowed to have one of the two values 0 or $-E$. If one or more of these voltages is at $-E$, so also is E_d. In this case, we may let A be the event that $E_a = -E$, etc. The relation between input and output is expressed by the single equation $D = A + B + C$.

The AND circuit may be realized by the configuration of Fig. 4-2. If the inputs are driven by low-impedance sources, the output voltage E_d is clamped at the highest of the values E_a, E_b, and E_c. Again, we suppose two values 0 and $-E$ are allowed, and that A is the event that $E_a = -E$, etc. The terminal relations are indicated in the single equation $D = ABC$.

The functions of the two circuits in Figs. 4-1 and 4-2 have been described in terms of the convention that $A = 1$ when $E_a = -E$

(i.e., when the input voltage at *a* is "down"), etc.   It is instructive to note that the roles of the AND and OR circuits are interchanged if the convention is that $A = 1$ when $E_a = 0$ (i.e., when the input at *a* is "up"), etc.   This interchange of function may be understood in terms of De Morgan's rule of complements (Table 3-1).

INHIBITOR Circuit. Before considering the NOT circuit, its relation to another simple Boolean function will be noted.   A practical form of the NOT circuit is the INHIBITOR circuit.   Figure 4-3 shows

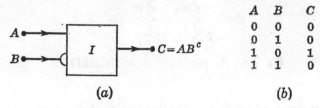

A	B	C
0	0	0
0	1	0
1	0	1
1	1	0

(a)   *(b)*

Fig. 4-3 The INHIBITOR circuit and its logic matrix.

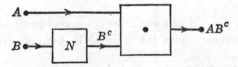

Fig. 4-4 Combination to form an IN-
            HIBITOR circuit.

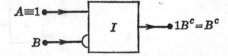

Fig. 4-5 A NOT circuit from an
            INHIBITOR.

a symbol for the INHIBITOR circuit and its logic matrix.   The terminal relations are summarized in the equation $C = AB^c$.   On the one hand, the INHIBITOR circuit may be achieved by the combination of a NOT circuit and an AND circuit as shown in Fig. 4-4.   If the input to the NOT circuit is B, the output is B^c.   If this output and A are the inputs to the AND circuit, the output of the latter must be AB^c.   On the other hand, if an INHIBITOR is available, maintaining the condition $A = 1$ insures that its output is $1B^c = B^c$.   Figure 4-5 illustrates this condition.

The last result is of interest because one practical form of the NOT circuit is achieved simply by using a triode vacuum tube as an INHIBITOR. A circuit is shown in Fig. 4-6. For a suitable choice of values of $-E_s$ and of the resistors, the tube will be cut off (and thus have very

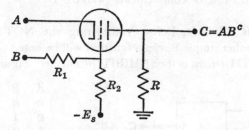

Fig. 4-6 A triode used as an INHIBITOR circuit.

high resistance) when $E_b = -E$. If $E_b = 0$, the output voltage E^c will be approximately E_a. These conditions provide the desired terminal relations.

We turn now to consider some other examples of switching functions obtained by combinations of the basic AND, OR, and NOT units.

EXCLUSIVE OR Circuit. The symbol of Fig. 4-7a indicates a circuit element which realizes the disjunctive union or EXCLUSIVE OR

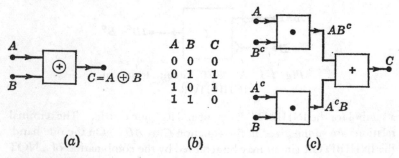

A	B	C
0	0	0
0	1	1
1	0	1
1	1	0

(a) *(b)* *(c)*

Fig. 4-7 The EXCLUSIVE OR circuit.

relationship. As the logic matrix of Fig. 4-7b shows, $C = 1$ if $A = 1$ or $B = 1$ but not both. The combination of AND and NOT circuits shown in Fig. 4-7c realizes this condition, provided both A and A^c, B

and B^c are available.   If the complements are not available, two NOT circuits are also required.   The circuit realizes the desired condition by virtue of the relation $C = AB^c + A^cB = A \oplus B$.   Since the EXCLU- SIVE OR relationship can be expressed in more than one way as a set or logic relation, more than one way of realizing the function in terms of AND, OR, NOT circuits should be available.   Also, it should be noted that it is not necessary to provide the complements if the AND circuits in Fig. 4-7c are replaced by INHIBITOR circuits.

COMPARATOR Circuit.   The circuit of Fig. 4-8 gives an output if any A_k fails to match the corresponding B_k.

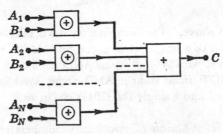

Fig. 4-8   A COMPARATOR circuit.

HALF ADDER.   The device, represented by the symbol and logic matrix of Fig. 4-9, is of use in the addition of binary numbers.   The

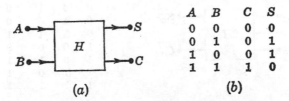

A	B	C	S
0	0	0	0
0	1	0	1
1	0	0	1
1	1	1	0

(a)   (b)

Fig. 4-9   The HALF ADDER and its logic matrix.

two outputs S and C (sum and carry) are defined by the logic matrix and may be expressed as the Boolean functions

$$S = A \oplus B = AB^c + A^cB = (A + B)(AB)^c$$
$$C = AB$$

The two functions could be realized separately by an AND circuit for C and an EXCLUSIVE OR circuit such as is shown in Fig. 4-7 for S. Another configuration which is more economical of circuit elements is shown in Fig. 4-10. This configuration is suggested by the last

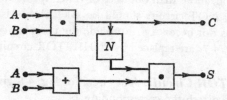

Fig. 4-10   A HALF ADDER from basic
logic elements.

expression for S above. The combination AB is necessary to produce the carry C. Use of a single NOT circuit provides $C^c = (AB)^c$, which may be combined with $A + B$ in an AND circuit, as shown. Note also that the NOT circuit and the AND circuit providing the output S may be combined into a single INHIBITOR circuit.

FULL ADDER. Addition of two binary numbers requires in each place, except possibly the lowest order place, addition of the two digits and a carry from the previous addition to produce a sum and a new

C_{n-1}	A_n	B_n	C_n	S_n
0	0	0	0	0
0	0	1	0	1
0	1	0	0	1
0	1	1	1	0
1	0	0	0	1
1	0	1	1	0
1	1	0	1	0
1	1	1	1	1

Fig. 4-11   The FULL ADDER and its logic matrix.

carry. The set of possible cases is exhibited in the logic matrix of Fig. 4-11. The device which accomplishes these combinations is known as a FULL ADDER. The symbol $2H$ is used, in anticipation of the fact that FULL ADDERS may be achieved by combinations of two HALF ADDERS. One possible configuration involving the latter is shown in Fig. 4-12. The FULL ADDER logic may be traced by considering the various possible sets of inputs C_{n-1}, A_n, B_n. Use of the logic matrices for the HALF ADDERS H_1 and H_2 makes it possible to determine the functions S^*, C^*, S^{**}, and C^{**}, and from these the outputs C_n and S_n. It is assumed that each component logic network is capable of driving the elements connected to its outputs.

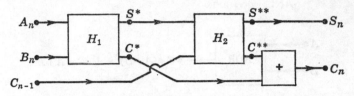

Fig. 4-12 A FULL ADDER from HALF ADDERS.

Other Logic Elements. The discussion above has assumed that the basic operations are AND, OR, and NOT (intersection, union, and complement; or product, sum, and negation). As a matter of fact, one can form any combination by use of the NOT operation and either the AND or the OR operation. Suppose devices are available to perform the AND and the NOT operations. The identity

$$A + B = (A^c B^c)^c$$

shows that the OR operation can be derived therefrom. Similarly, the identity

$$AB = (A^c + B^c)^c$$

shows that the AND operation can be derived from the OR and NOT operations.

The question naturally arises whether there is a single operation from which all operations may be derived. Three such operations may be listed: the INHIBITOR, the NOR (NOT OR), and the NAND (NOT AND). The INHIBITOR operation can produce the AND and NOT operations by virtue of the identities: If $A = 1$,

$$AB^c = B^c$$

Also, $$AB = A(B^c)^c$$

These equations are realized by the INHIBITOR circuit configurations shown in Fig. 4-13.

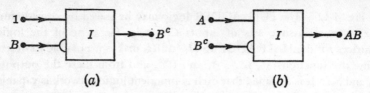

Fig. 4-13   Use of the INHIBITOR circuit to obtain the NOT and AND operations.

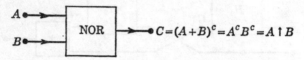

Fig. 4-14   The NOR (NOT OR) circuit.

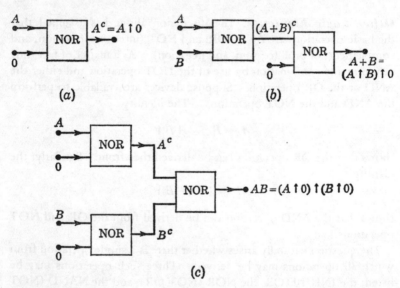

Fig. 4-15   Realization of basic logic elements with the NOR circuit.

The NOR and the NAND operations correspond to operations known in works on logic as the *Sheffer stroke functions* [Ref. 15, pp. 68ff.]. Symbols and logical relations are as follows:

$$A \downarrow B = (AB)^c \qquad \text{(NAND)}$$
$$A \uparrow B = (A + B)^c \qquad \text{(NOR)}$$

It is quite obvious that the NOR relation can be derived from the NOT and OR relations. Figure 4-14 shows a representation of a NOR element. Figure 4-15 shows how NOT, OR, and AND operations can be achieved through the use of NOR circuits. The configurations in Fig. 4-15a to c correspond to the expressions

$$A \uparrow 0 = A^c$$
$$A + B = (A \uparrow B)^c = (A \uparrow B) \uparrow 0$$
$$AB = A^c \uparrow B^c = (A \uparrow 0) \uparrow (B \uparrow 0)$$

Thus, any Boolean function can be built up by use of the Sheffer stroke operation $\uparrow$. A similar situation holds for the other Sheffer stroke operation. Simple, practical NOR circuits have been developed commercially. The use of one type of unit is sufficient to develop all types of logic networks. Even if somewhat more complicated networks should be required, there is the practical advantage of having to stock only one kind of component as a spare part for such systems.

4-2. *Majority and Minority Logic Devices*

In this section we consider a somewhat different class of logic elements. Simple schematic representations of the basic devices are shown in Fig. 4-16. The various inputs and outputs of the devices are assumed to have the values 0 or 1. As in the case of the logic devices considered in Sec. 4-1, we may visualize these as voltages (with respect to a fixed reference) appearing at the terminals. The inputs are weighted according to the numbers shown at the inputs (w_k on the diagrams). We shall assume the weights are positive integers (or perhaps 0). The output values are determined by the pattern of input values and by the weights assigned to the different inputs. The variable B is called a *bias* and is held constant at 0 or 1.

Consider the *majority element* shown in Fig. 4-16a. It has inputs V_0, V_1, V_2, and B, with corresponding weights w_0, w_1, w_2, and w_3. If we let S be the weighted sum of the inputs

$$S = \sum_{k=0}^{2} w_k V_k + w_3 B$$

and let T be one-half the sum of the weights

$$T = \frac{1}{2} \sum_{k=0}^{3} w_k$$

then the output $D = 1$, iffi $S > T$; otherwise, $D = 0$. Thus there is an output iffi the weighted inputs present constitute a majority of the possible total weighted inputs. The value T is the *threshold* value which the weighted inputs must exceed to obtain an output different from 0. The summation formulas are written in a manner to indicate

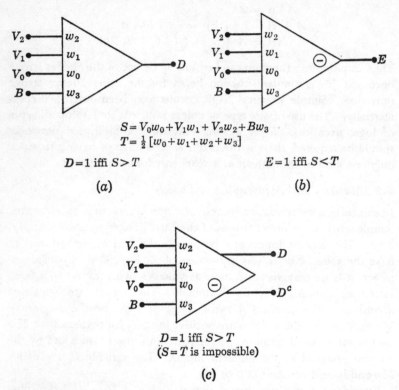

$$S = V_0w_0 + V_1w_1 + V_2w_2 + Bw_3$$
$$T = \tfrac{1}{2}[w_0 + w_1 + w_2 + w_3]$$

$D = 1$ iffi $S > T$ $E = 1$ iffi $S < T$

(a)   *(b)*

$D = 1$ iffi $S > T$
$(S = T$ is impossible$)$

(c)

Fig. 4-16   *(a)* Majority, *(b)* minority, and *(c)* combined minority-majority logic elements.

how the expressions would generalize for N variables $V_0, V_1, \ldots, V_{N-1}$ and a bias B.

The unit shown in Fig. 4-16*b* has a symbol which differs from the majority element symbol by the addition of the encircled minus sign at the output terminal. This unit is called a *minority element* since there is an output iffi the weighted inputs present constitute a minority of the possible total weighted inputs. Stated another way, the sum of the weighted inputs must be less than the threshold value T to obtain an output different from 0. In symbols, $E = 1$ iffi $S < T$. If, as is usually the case, it is impossible to have $S = T$, and if the majority and minority units have the same inputs and weights, it is apparent that $E = D^c$. In many practical devices it is feasible to have both D and D^c as outputs. Such a device is indicated by the symbol in Fig. 4-16c. The device is a majority element with respect to the output marked D and a minority device with respect to the output D^c. The latter is indicated by the encircled minus sign. It is assumed for such a unit that the weights are such that the condition $S = T$ is impossible.

In most systems utilizing minority-majority elements, it is feasible to have both the variable and its complement for each of the driving variables. Thus, if A_3 is a driving variable, it is reasonable to assume that both A_3 and A_3^c are available as suitable physical signals. In order to indicate symbolically the Boolean functions generated by a majority or minority element, it is convenient to adopt a hybrid notation. For a majority element, as in Fig. 4-16a, we write

$$D = \text{maj}(w_0 V_0, \ w_1 V_1, \ w_2 V_2, \ w_3 B)$$

and for a minority element, as in Fig. 4-16b, we write

$$E = \text{mnr}(w_0 V_0, \ w_1 V_1, \ w_2 V_2, \ w_3 B)$$

Suppose, for example, w_0, w_1, w_2, w_3 have the values 1, 1, 3, 2, respectively, and the input variables V_0, V_1, V_2, B have the values 1, 0, 0, 1. Then

$$D = \text{maj}[1 \cdot 1, \ 1 \cdot 0, \ 3 \cdot 0, \ 2 \cdot 1] = 0$$

since only three of a possible seven weights are present at the input. On the other hand, for this same pattern

$$E = \text{mnr}[1 \cdot 1, \ 1 \cdot 0, \ 3 \cdot 0, \ \ 2 \cdot 1] = 1 = D^c$$

since only a minority of the possible input weights is present.

Examples We consider some simple examples to illustrate the behavior and to demonstrate a systematic method of analysis using function designation numbers and *weighted function designation numbers*.

First we show that the basic logic circuits, NOT, OR, and AND, may be derived from minority elements.   The NOT circuit of Fig. 4-17a is quite simple.   A minority of the possible inputs is 0.   An output thus appears only when the input is 0.

For the element of Fig. 4-17b, we may make the following analysis, in terms of function designation numbers.

$$
\begin{array}{ll}
A,B & 3210 \\
A^c & 0011 \\
B^c & 0101 \\
0 & 0000 \\
S\ (T = \tfrac{3}{2}) & 0112 \\
\mathrm{Mnr}(A^c,B^c,1 \cdot 0) & 1110 \\
A + B & 1110
\end{array}
$$

The minority row is obtained by considering in each place the sum of the weighted values A^c, B^c, 0 and comparing with the possible sum 3.

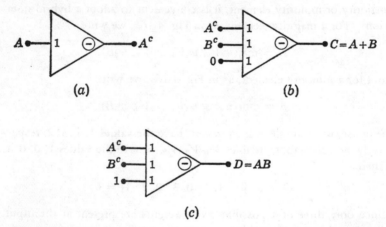

$$(a) \qquad\qquad (b)$$

$$(c)$$

Fig. 4-17   Basic logic elements from minority elements: (a) NOT circuit, (b) OR circuit, and (c) AND circuit.

If the weighted sum is 0 or 1, the minority function has the value 1. Otherwise, the minority function has the value 0.   Comparison with the designator for the function $A + B$ shows that the latter function is indeed generated, as indicated in Fig. 4-17b.

A similar analysis of the element represented in Fig. 4-17c shows it to be an AND circuit.

A,B	3210
A^o	0011
B^c	0101
1	1111
$S\ (T = \tfrac{3}{2})$	1223
$\mathrm{Mnr}(A^c,B^c,1)$	1000
AB	1000

The circuit of Fig. 4-18 shows a FULL ADDER circuit derived from

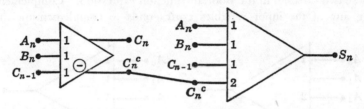

Fig. 4-18 FULL ADDER from minority-majority elements.

one mixed unit and one majority unit.   This circuit may be analyzed as
follows.

First unit:

A_n,B_n,C_{n-1}	7654	3210
A_n	1111	0000
B_n	1100	1100
C_{n-1}	1010	1010
$S\ (T = \tfrac{3}{2})$	3221	2110
$\mathrm{Maj}(A_n,B_n,C_{n-1})$	1110	1000
C_n	1110	1000
$C_n{}^c$	0001	0111

Second unit:

A_n,B_n,C_{n-1}	7654	3210
A_n	1111	0000
B_n	1100	1100
C_{n-1}	1010	1010
$2C_n{}^c$	0002	0222
$S\ (T = \tfrac{5}{2})$	3223	2332
$\mathrm{Maj}(A_n,B_n,C_{n-1},2C_n{}^c)$	1001	0110
S_n	1001	0110

In the second unit we encounter for the first time an input weight other than 1. Corresponding to this input we use the weighted designator, which automatically provides the weight when summing in each place.

In Fig. 4-19 are shown two cases of four input majority elements with a minimum total input weight. In order to avoid the possibility of making $S = T$, we keep the sum of the weights odd. The two essential cases are shown. For a given bias weight and value, the interchange of connections of any two of the A_k corresponds to the interchange of these two variables in the Boolean function expression. Complementing any of the input variables corresponds to complementing that

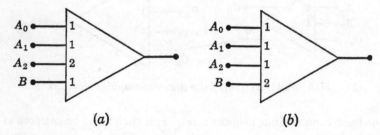

(a)   (b)

Fig. 4-19 A four-input majority element with minimum allowable weights, with bias weighted (*a*) unity and (*b*) 2.

variable in the Boolean function expression. Consider the system in Fig. 4-19*a*. We may analyze it as follows:

A_2, A_1, A_0	7654 3210	7654 3210
B	1111 1111	0000 0000
$2A_2$	2222 0000	2222 0000
A_1	1100 1100	1100 1100
A_0	1010 1010	1010 1010
$S\ (T = \frac{5}{2})$	5443 3220	4332 2110
Maj	1111 1000	1110 0000

$$B = 1 \qquad n_F = 1111\ 1000 \qquad F = A_2 + A_2{}^c A_1 A_0$$
$$B = 0 \qquad n_F = 1110\ 0000 \qquad F = A_2(A_1 + A_0)$$

If, for example, we wished to generate the function $A^c(B + C)$ with a majority element, we could choose the configuration of Fig. 4-19*a*; in this circuit we put bias at 0, connect A^c to the terminal weighted 2, and connect B and C to the two remaining terminals having weight 1. An analysis similar to that above may be made for the configuration of Fig. 4-19*b*.

Let us now consider how an EXCLUSIVE OR circuit may be constructed from minority-majority elements. We have already noted that

$$A \oplus B = (A + B)(AB)^c$$

Also, configurations for developing $A + B$, AB, and $(AB)^c$ have been considered. Fig. 4-20*a* shows one possible combination of elements

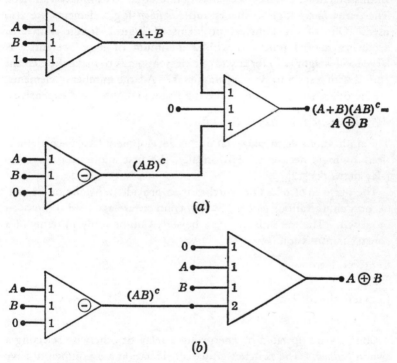

Fig. 4-20 Two realizations of the EXCLUSIVE OR circuit.

to develop the EXCLUSIVE OR circuit. A majority element and a minority element are used to generate $A + B$ and $(AB)^c$, respectively. These are combined in a third element which takes the product of the two inputs $A + B$ and $(AB)^c$ to produce $A \oplus B$. A somewhat more efficient circuit is shown in Fig. 4-20*b*. The function $(AB)^c$ is generated as in the previously discussed circuit. This is combined with A and B

in a four-input majority element in the manner discussed above to provide the desired combination.

It is not possible within the scope of this work to discuss the circuitry involved in minority-majority elements. For many applications, this type of circuitry has advantages in terms of cost, reliability, and system complexity over the logic elements of the type discussed in Sec. 4-1. Considerable attention has been given in the engineering literature to both circuit and logical design of elements and systems. In this literature, these devices are often referred to as *threshold* devices. The terms *linear* logic elements and *Kirchhoff* logic elements are also used. One of the principal problems of logical design is that of achieving desired functions with a minimum of input weights. A large total weight $(2T)$ for any single element tends to make the element critical with respect to system parameters. A large number of elements, on the other hand, tends to make the system complex and expensive.

4-3. *Relay and Switching Circuits*

The applications discussed so far in this development have been applications to logic networks. Historically, the first applications were to relay networks [12].

The purpose of relays or switches is to provide transmission or connection along various paths. Switch contacts are assumed to be open or closed. The transmission may be stated numerically in terms of a contact transmission factor T:

Contacts open:

$$T = 0$$

Contacts closed:

$$T = 1$$

Contacts are operated by energizing a relay or otherwise selecting a switch *position*. The switches under consideration are assumed to have two positions: *operated* and *unoperated*. We may designate a switch by a capital letter A and suppose the *event A* is the event that the switch A is operated. The Boolean algebra may be introduced by representing the two possible positions by the Boolean *position variable* as follows:

Switch A unoperated:

$$A = 0$$

Switch A operated:

$$A = 1$$

The contact transmission factor T can be expressed simply as a Boolean function of the position variable. The situation is shown in Fig. 4-21. The two cases may be summarized:

Normally open contacts:

$$T = A$$

Normally closed contacts:

$$T = A^c$$

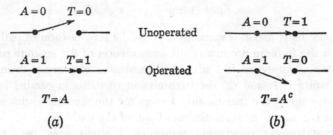

Fig. 4-21 Contact transmission functions for (a) normally open and (b) normally closed contacts.

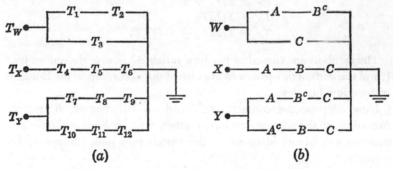

Fig. 4-22 Transmissions for a switching network.

The scheme developed above makes it possible to designate the transmission of each set of contacts on a given switch or relay A by the appropriate symbol A or A^c.

In order to see how this scheme applies to switching networks, consider the example in Fig. 4-22a. It is desired to establish connection or transmission from the various input points to a common terminal indicated as ground. The switching conditions may be indicated by indicating the values 0 or 1 for the various contact transmission factors $T_1, T_2, \ldots, T_{12}$. If we let T_W be the transmission factor indicating whether the W input is connected to ground, we must have

$$T_W = 1 \text{ iffi } T_1 = 1 \text{ and } T_2 = 1 \text{ or } T_3 = 1$$

In a similar manner we may designate transmission factors T_X and T_Y. For these we have the relations:

$$T_X = 1 \text{ iffi } T_4 = 1 \text{ and } T_5 = 1 \text{ and } T_6 = 1$$
$$T_Y = 1 \text{ iffi } T_7 = 1 \text{ and } T_8 = 1 \text{ and } T_9 = 1$$
$$\text{or } T_{10} = 1 \text{ and } T_{11} = 1 \text{ and } T_{12} = 1$$

This example makes it apparent that (1) the transmission of paths in series is the Boolean product of the transmission of the separate paths, since the transmission is 1 iffi the transmission of every path in the series string is 1; and (2) the transmission of paths in parallel is the Boolean sum of the transmission factors for the separate paths, since contact is made if the transmission of any of the paths is 1.

The statements concerning transmission above may be written compactly as Boolean functions:

$$T_W = T_1 T_2 + T_3$$
$$T_X = T_4 T_5 T_6$$
$$T_Y = T_7 T_8 T_9 + T_{10} T_{11} T_{12}$$

The symbols are viewed as Boolean variables, having the values 0 or 1, and the arithmetic operations are carried out according to the Boolean arithmetic schedules.

Now suppose the contacts are found on switches A, B, and C. According to the scheme developed earlier, we may express the contact transmission factors in terms of the switch positions. Suppose, for example,

$T_1 = T_4 = T_7 = A$	Normally open contacts on switch A
$T_{10} = A^c$	Normally closed contact on switch A
$T_5 = T_{11} = B$	Normally open contacts on switch B
$T_2 = T_8 = B^c$	Normally closed contacts on switch B
$T_3 = T_6 = T_9 = T_{12} = C$	Normally open contacts on switch C

The transmission factors may be written

$$W = AB^c + C$$
$$X = ABC$$
$$Y = AB^cC + A^cBC$$

The first indicates that input W is connected if both switch A is closed and switch B is open or if switch C is closed. The second indicates that input X is connected if switches A, B, and C are all closed. A similar interpretation may be made for input Y. It is customary to label the switch-connection diagram as in Fig. 4-22b, which shows the various

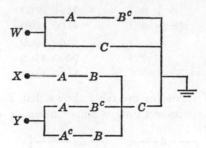

Fig. 4-23   Alternate switching network realizing the same
switching function as
that of Figure 4-22b.

contact transmission factors as the appropriate functions of the switch positions.

Manipulation of the Boolean functions for the various transmissions into different forms suggests different equivalent switching arrangements. For example, we may write

$$X = (AB)C$$
$$Y = (AB^c + A^cB)C$$

This suggests making a single C contact common for the paths from inputs X and Y, as in Fig. 4-23. The result is a saving of two contacts on switch C. This arrangement preserves the isolation of inputs X and Y, for the Boolean algebra shows that they cannot be connected to the single C contact at the same time. This follows from the fact that

$$AB(AB^c + A^cB) = 0$$

Other combinations may be found by manipulation of the algebraic expressions.

As a further example, consider the circuit of Fig. 4-24a. This circuit obeys the switching function

$$T = (A + BC^c)(AB + A^cC) + A^cB = T_1 + A^cB$$

We may analyze the function as follows

A,B,C	7654 3210
A	1111 0000
B	1100 1100
C	1010 1010
$A + BC^c$	1111 0100
$AB + A^cC$	1100 1010
T_1	1100 0000
A^cB	0000 1100
T	1100 1100

Comparison of entries in the table shows that $T = B$. Thus the switching function requires only a single normally open switch (or

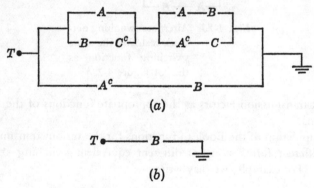

(a)

(b)

Fig. 4-24   Simplification of a switching circuit: (*a*) original circuit and (*b*) simplified circuit.

relay).   The positions of switches A and C have no effect on the circuit connection.

The simplification of this switching circuit could have been carried out by trial and error.   A circuit could have been built or the paths traced on the diagram and the transmission for each of the possible switch positions noted.   The symbolic analysis above, however, is obviously easier and cheaper.   As a matter of fact, the tabular analysis was used to obtain this example, which simplifies in such a dramatic fashion.

The general discussion and examples have indicated that there is a natural correlation between the form of the switching configuration and the form of the switching function. Use of the algebra and various associated techniques enables one to discover different forms of the switching function to which correspond various switching circuits with equivalent operational characteristics. One of the objectives of such manipulation is the reduction of the number of switch contacts needed to perform switching functions. This objective may be coupled with the aim of approximate equalization of the number of contacts on the various switches, or at least the limiting of the number of contacts on any one switch.

This brief introductory treatment cannot illustrate the variety of special problems and techniques which may be encountered in practical design. For one thing, it should be noted that the analysis has been combinatorial, in the sense that it does not take into account time sequences. Problems which arise when relay closing times and sequences of operation are important require much more extensive analysis. Combinatorial analysis may be invaluable in the process of analysis and synthesis of such sequential circuits, however, so that the procedures developed and extensions thereof provide important background material. For a comprehensive treatment of the problems of logical design of switching circuits, consult Ref. 3.

Problems

4-1 Represent the Boolean functions listed below by networks of AND, OR, and NOT circuits.

   (a) $AB + A^cB^c$
   (b) $(A + B^c + C)(A^c + B + C^c)(A^c + B^c + C^c)$
   (c) $(A + B)[C^c + F^c(D + E)]$
$$+ A[C^cD^cE^c + (C + F)(D + E)]$$

4-2 Using AND, OR, and NOT elements, draw a logic network corresponding to each of the two forms of the function shown below. Assume that the variables A, B, C, D, E and their complements are available as driving variables.

$$(A^cE + BE^c)C + (ABC^c + A^cB^cC^c)E^c = A^cC + ABE^c$$

4-3 Use HALF-ADDER logic and derive the logic matrix for configuration of Fig. 4-12. Verify that this is FULL-ADDER logic.

4-4 Write logic matrices for $A \uparrow B$ and $A \downarrow B$.

4-5 **(a)** Show that a NOR circuit may be derived from AND and NOT circuits; and show that AND and NOT circuits may be derived from NOR circuits.

     (b) Show that AND and NOT circuits may be used to obtain NAND circuits; and show that NAND circuits may be used to obtain AND and NOT circuits.

     (c) Repeat part **(b)** with OR and NOT circuits.

4-6 **(a)** Consider a majority device with inputs A, B, and C each given the weight 1. Determine the switching function.

     (b) Let C be a bias input (i.e., identically 0 or identically 1) and show that AND and OR circuits result.

4-7 **(a)** Suppose A is connected to a minority-majority element with weight w_1 and A^c is connected to the same unit with weight w_2, with $w_2 < w_1$. Show that the effect is the same as connecting A and a bias with appropriate weights.

     (b) What is the effect if $w_1 < w_2$?

4-8 **(a)** Analyze the four-input majority element of Fig. 4-19b. Determine the two switching functions corresponding to the cases $B = 0$ and $B = 1$, respectively.

     (b) What functions are developed if A_0 is replaced by A_0^c and A_1 by A_1^c?

     (c) Show the corrections required to develop the function

$$(A^cB)^c + C$$

(Note that the B in this expression is not the bias B.)

4-9 Show how to obtain NOR and NAND circuits from majority or minority elements.

4-10 Give a set (event) formulation to the relay problem. Describe the elementary events and the more important events used in expressing the problem.

4-11 Represent the Boolean functions listed below by appropriate switching networks whose transmissions are given by the corresponding functions:

     (a) $A(B^c + CD) + A^cB(C + D)$
     (b) $A(B + C)(D + EF) + A^cBCE$

(c) $AB + (AB)^c + A^cB^c$

(d) $(A + B^c + C)(A^c + B + C^c)(A + B + C)$

(e) $(A + B)[C^c + F(D + E^c)] + A^c[CDE^c + (C + F)(DE)^c]$

4-12 Represent the various Boolean functions of Prob. 4-1 by appropriate switching networks whose transmissions are given by the corresponding Boolean functions.

4-13 Repeat Prob. 4-2 using switches or relays and interpreting the Boolean functions as transmissions to ground.

4-14 Write the Boolean functions for the transmissions for the various switching circuits shown in Fig. P4-14.

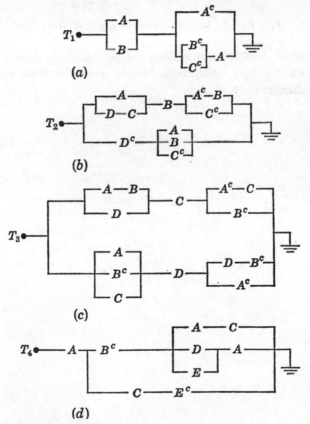

Fig. P4-14 Switching circuits for Prob. 4-14.

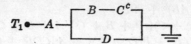

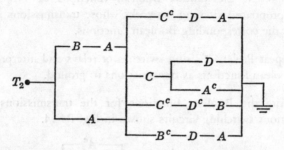

Fig. P4-15 Switching circuits for Prob. 4-15.

4-15 Write the Boolean functions for the switching circuits in Fig. P4-15. Show that these circuits have the same switching characteristics.

Extensions and Generalizations

Chapter 5

In this chapter, we consider several topics of theoretical interest and generalize certain concepts discussed in earlier chapters. The primary aim of the chapter is to provide some glimpse of the range and power of the theory of sets as a mathematical discipline. The choice of material is limited and somewhat arbitrary, but is made with a view to providing material useful as a background for the mathematical theory of probability (as a special case of measure theory).

Readers interested primarily in applications to problems of switching may wish to ignore this chapter. Also, it should be pointed out that the usual treatment of the applications of probability theory do not make much use of the ideas and techniques of this chapter. The teaching experience of the author has indicated the desirability of a much more thorough treatment of fundamental ideas than is customary for those who would exploit most fully the mathematical theory of probability. Some modern treatments for engineers and scientists, such as Ref. 10, have made considerable progress in this direction. An acquaintance with the material of this chapter should make such treatments easier to master.

5-1. *Sequences and Limits*

For many problems involving classes of sets—notably in the theory of measure and probability—the concept of a limit of a sequence of sets plays an important role. The concept of a limit in abstract set theory is distinct from the notion of a limit in real variable theory, although some relationships between them may be traced. We shall simply state the appropriate definitions and discuss these briefly.

Let $A_1, A_2, \ldots$ be a sequence of sets in some universal set U. We do not necessarily assume the sets to be distinct. The *limit inferior* of the sequence, denoted by $\lim \inf A_k$ or by $\underline{\lim} A_k$, is the set A_* of those elements x which are in all but a finite number of the sets A_k of the sequence.

If an element x is in all but a finite number of the A_k, then there is a number n such that x is in

$$\bigcap_{k=n}^{\infty} A_k$$

and conversely, if x is in some such intersection, it is in the limit inferior. We thus have the important formula

$$A_* = \lim \inf A_k = \bigcup_{n=1}^{\infty} \bigcap_{k=n}^{\infty} A_k$$

It is apparent that the limit inferior always exists, although it may be the null set.

For the same sequence, we may also define the *limit superior* of the sequence, written $\lim \sup A_k$ or $\overline{\lim} A_k$, to be the set A^* consisting of all those elements x which are in an infinite number of the A_k.

If an element x is in an infinite number of the A_k, then no matter what integer n is chosen the element is in some A_k for $k \geq n$. This means that for every n we have x in the union

$$\bigcup_{k=n}^{\infty} A_k$$

On the other hand, if x is in this union for every n, it must be in an infinite number of the A_k. Hence we have the formula

$$A^* = \lim \sup A_k = \bigcap_{n=1}^{\infty} \bigcup_{k=n}^{\infty} A_k$$

It should be apparent from the definitions that $A_* \subset A^*$, for if x belongs to all but a finite number of the A_k, it must belong to an infinite number. The following examples show that the opposite inclusion relation does not always hold, however.

Suppose A_k is a sequence of nonempty sets and that B is a nonempty set having no points in common with any A_k (i.e., $A_k B = \emptyset$ for each k). Form a new sequence B_k as follows:

$$\text{For } k \text{ odd, put } B_k = A_k$$
$$\text{For } k \text{ even, put } B_k = A_k + B$$

Then $B \subset B^*$, but $BB_* = \emptyset$; that is, every point in B is also in B^*, but no point of B is in B_*. Thus $B^* \not\subset B_*$.

As a second example, consider two sets A and B. Let $\{A_k\}$ be the sequence such that $A_k = A$ for k odd, and $A_k = B$ for k even. An examination of the formulas derived from the definitions shows that $A_* = AB$ and $A^* = A + B$. Again it is apparent that in general these are not equal but that always $A_* \subset A^*$.

It is apparent from the definitions that A_* and A^* are not altered by the alteration (or removal) of any finite number of members of the sequence $\{A_k\}$.

There are important sequences for which the limit inferior and the limit superior are the same set. Such sequences are said to be *convergent* and the common set which is both the limit superior and the limit inferior is referred to as the *limit* of the sequence, denoted $\lim A_k$.

A sequence A_k is referred to as an *expanding sequence* iffi for each k we have $A_k \subset A_{k+1}$. Similarly, the sequence is said to be a *contracting sequence* iffi for each k we have $A_k \supset A_{k+1}$. In either case we refer to the sequence as a *monotone sequence*. Every monotone sequence has a limit.

For an expanding sequence:

$$\lim A_k = \bigcup_{k=1}^{\infty} A_k$$

For a contracting sequence:

$$\lim A_k = \bigcap_{k=1}^{\infty} A_k$$

These results may be obtained from the formulas derived from the definitions. For the expanding case, we note that

$$\bigcap_{k=n}^{\infty} A_k = A_n \quad \text{and} \quad \bigcup_{k=n}^{\infty} A_k = \bigcup_{k=1}^{\infty} A_k$$

Substitution in the formulas yields the desired results. On the other hand, for a contracting sequence we have

$$\bigcap_{k=n}^{\infty} A_k = \bigcap_{k=1}^{\infty} A_k \quad \text{and} \quad \bigcup_{k=n}^{\infty} A_k = A_n$$

from which the formula for the limit follows.

5-2. *Additive Classes of Sets*

Among the more important kinds of classes of sets are those known as *additive classes*. An additive class of sets is also referred to in the literature by the term *field* (of sets) and by the term *algebra of sets*. The latter usage is to be distinguished from the algebra of set operations discussed in earlier chapters. We begin by stating the definition.

A nonempty class $\mathcal{C}$ of sets is called an *additive class of sets* provided the following conditions hold:

(i) If $A_1, A_2, \ldots, A_n$ is any finite sequence of members of the class $\mathcal{C}$, their union is also a member of $\mathcal{C}$.

(ii) If A is any set in the class $\mathcal{C}$, its complement A^c is also in $\mathcal{C}$.

These conditions are often summarized briefly in words by saying that an additive class $\mathcal{C}$ is a class closed under the formation of finite unions and of complements.

If the condition (i) is enlarged to allow infinite sequences, so that the class is closed under the formation of countably infinite unions, the class is referred to as a *completely additive class*. The terms corresponding to the alternatives above are *field* or *σ-field* and *σ-algebra*.

As a first step toward seeing the nature of the additive class, we list a number of properties which are so basic that we number them in the same list as the defining properties.

(iii) The universal set U belongs to $\mathcal{C}$.

Since the class is nonempty, there is at least one set A in the class. By Property (ii) its complement A^c is also in the class. But by Property (i) it follows that $U = A + A^c$ belongs to $\mathcal{C}$.

(iv) The empty set $\emptyset$ belongs to $\mathcal{C}$.

This is an immediate consequence of Properties (iii) and (ii).

(v) If the members of the finite sequence $A_1, A_2, \ldots, A_n$ belong to $\mathcal{C}$, so does their intersection.

By Property (ii), each of the sets $A_1^c, A_2^c, \ldots, A_n^c$ belongs to $\mathcal{C}$. By Property (i) the union of this latter class belongs to α as does the complement of this union by Property (ii). Use of De Morgan's rule gives the result

$$\bigcap_{k=1}^{n} A_k = (\bigcup_{k=1}^{n} A_k^c)^c \in \alpha$$

It is apparent that the arguments above hold without change for countable unions and intersections. For completely additive classes we may add the important theorems:

(vi) If $\{A_k\}$ is a sequence of members of class α, it follows that $A_* = \lim \inf A_k$ and $A^* = \lim \sup A_k$ must belong to α.

These results follow from the properties above and the formulas for A_* and A^* derived from the definitions.

(vii) If $\{A_k\}$ is a sequence of members of class α for which

$$A = \lim A_k$$

exists, then A must belong to α. This follows directly from (vi) and definitions.

These basic theorems serve to indicate something of the extent and flexibility of completely additive classes with respect to basic set operations. The list is fundamental but far from exhaustive.

As a simple example of an additive class, consider the space U consisting of three elements $\{x_1, x_2, x_3\}$. Define the sets

$$A_1 = \{x_1\} \qquad A_2 = \{x_2\} \qquad A_3 = \{x_3\}$$
$$A_{12} = \{x_1, x_2\} \qquad A_{13} = \{x_1, x_3\} \qquad A_{23} = \{x_2, x_3\}$$

The class α of all possible subsets of U consists of eight sets.

$$\alpha = \{\emptyset, A_1, A_2, A_3, A_{12}, A_{13}, A_{23}, U\}$$

Examination of each of the eight sets shows the class is closed under the formation of complements. For example, $A_1^c = A_{23}$ and $A_{13}^c = A_2$. The union of any number of subsets is one of the subsets (including, of course, $\emptyset$ and U as subsets). Thus, the class is a completely additive class.

As a matter of fact, if U consists of any finite number N of elements, the class α of all subsets has 2^N members and is a completely additive class.

Another example of an additive class is developed in Sec. 5-4.

The intersection of any number of completely additive classes is itself a completely additive class. To see this, consider a family $\{\mathcal{C}_\alpha\}$, $\alpha \in I$, of completely additive classes. Here I is an arbitrary index set. If A is in each $\mathcal{C}_\alpha$, so also is A^c. If each member of the sequence $A_1, A_2, \ldots$ is in each $\mathcal{C}_\alpha$, so also is the union of the members of this sequence. Thus the intersection of the classes is closed under the formation of countable unions and complements. This fact leads to the concept of the *completely additive class generated by a class of sets*. If $\mathcal{B}$ is any class of sets, then the completely additive class generated by $\mathcal{B}$ is the intersection of all completely additive classes which contain $\mathcal{B}$. If $\mathcal{B}$ is itself a completely additive class, the generated class is also $\mathcal{B}$.

A very important example in the theory of measure and probability is the class of *Borel sets* on the real line. This is the completely additive class generated by the class of all open intervals (a,b) on the real line, where $(a,b) = \{x: a < x < b\}$. The argument below shows that this class includes all sets of the form $(-\infty,b) = \{x: x < b\}$, $(-\infty,b] = \{x: x \leq b\}$, $(a,b] = \{x: a < x \leq b\}$, and $[a,b] = \{x: a \leq x \leq b\}$. We note first that

$$(-\infty,b) = \bigcup_{n=1}^{\infty} (-n,b)$$

Any x in the semi-infinite interval is in all of the intervals $(-n,b)$ for n sufficiently large (say, $n > |x|$). If x is in the set denoted by the right hand member, it is in the interval $(-n,b)$ for some n and hence must be in the semi-infinite interval. A similar examination shows that

$$(-\infty,b] = \bigcap_{n=1}^{\infty} \left(-\infty, b + \frac{1}{n}\right)$$

We then note that

$$(a,b] = (-\infty,b](-\infty,a]^c$$

and

$$[a,b] = (-\infty,b](-\infty,a)^c$$

In each case, the set is built up by taking complements, unions, or intersections of sets in the completely additive class. Thus each of the derived sets is also a Borel set (i.e., a member of the completely additive class). It is not difficult to complete the line of reasoning above to establish the fact that the class of Borel sets is the completely additive class generated by the class of all intervals of the form $(-\infty, b]$, $(-\infty, b)$, $(a, b]$, or $[a, b]$.

5-3. *Some Properties of Inverse Functions or Transformations*

In the discussion of point functions in Sec. 2-1, it is noted that both the domain set and the range set may be subsets of abstract spaces. In this section we wish to emphasize this fact by using the term *(point) transformation.*

We consider the point transformation T whose domain D is a subset of the universal set U which has elements x. To each x in D there corresponds one and only one element y of the universal set (or space) V. The range of T is taken to be R, a subset of V. As in previous discussions in Sec. 2-1, we define the inverse transformation T^{-1} by the properties

$$T^{-1}(y) = \{x: T(x) = y\}$$
$$T^{-1}(B) = \{x: T(x) \in B\} \qquad B \subset V$$

If the range R is a proper subset of V, we suppose

$$T^{-1}(B) = T^{-1}(BR)$$

That is, the inverse image of a set B is the inverse image of that subset of B which lies in the range R of the transformation.

If the domain D of T is the whole space U and if the range R is the whole space V, we say T is a transformation from U *onto* V. Always, T is a transformation of D onto R. In case the range space R is a proper subset of V, we say that T is a transformation from D *into* V. It is sometimes convenient to designate the various cases by the following scheme:

$$T: U \text{ onto } V \qquad \text{or} \qquad T: D \text{ into } V \qquad \text{etc.}$$

The inverse transformation is taken in one case as a transformation that carries a point y into a subset of U and in the other case as a set transformation which carries a subset of V into a subset of U. It would be more precise logically to adopt consistently the latter point of view and write $T^{-1}(\{y\})$ rather than $T^{-1}(y)$. Use of the simpler notation is well established and its significance is quite clear. The mappings produced by a transformation T and its inverse T^{-1} are indicated schematically in Fig. 5-1. The diagram is intended to represent the

University of Pittsburgh
Bradford Campus Library

following relationships:

$$T^{-1}(y_1) = \{x_1, x_2\} \qquad T^{-1}(B_1) = A_1$$
$$T^{-1}(y_2) = \{x_3\} \qquad\quad T^{-1}(B_2) = A_2$$
$$T^{-1}(y_3) = \{x_4, x_5, x_6\} \qquad T^{-1}(B_3) = A_3$$
$$T^{-1}(y_4) = \{x_7\}$$

We now consider a number of important properties of inverse transformations. In the statements of these properties, we shall use an abbreviated notation which omits the index symbol. Thus, to consider the union of a class of sets of which A is a typical member, we shall

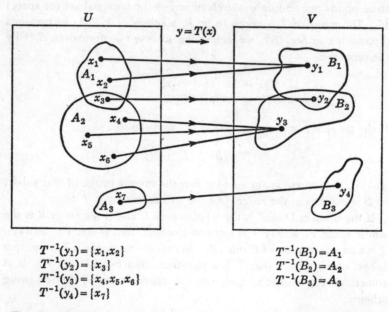

$$T^{-1}(y_1) = \{x_1, x_2\} \qquad\qquad T^{-1}(B_1) = A_1$$
$$T^{-1}(y_2) = \{x_3\} \qquad\qquad\quad T^{-1}(B_2) = A_2$$
$$T^{-1}(y_3) = \{x_4, x_5, x_6\} \qquad\quad T^{-1}(B_3) = A_3$$
$$T^{-1}(y_4) = \{x_7\}$$

Fig. 5-1 Mappings produced by a transformation T and its inverse T^{-1}.

simply write $\cup A$. The class may be finite, countably infinite, or uncountably infinite, unless specific conditions are imposed. Where possible, we let B indicate subsets of the range space V and A subsets of the domain space U.

(T1) $T^{-1}(\cup B) = \cup T^{-1}(B)$

        The inverse image of the union of a class is the union of the inverse images of the members of the class.

(T2) $T^{-1}(\cap B) = \cap T^{-1}(B)$

> The inverse image of the intersection of a class is the intersection of the inverse images of the members of the class.

(T3) $T^{-1}(B^c) = [T^{-1}(B)]^c$

> The inverse image of the complement of a set is the complement of the inverse image of the set.

These facts are illustrated in Fig. 5-1. For example,

$$T^{-1}(B_1 + B_2) = A_1 + A_2 = T^{-1}(B_1) + T^{-1}(B_2)$$

Similarly, $\qquad T^{-1}(B_1 B_2) = A_1 A_2 = T^{-1}(B_1)T^{-1}(B_2)$

Proofs of the properties above amount to little more than a careful reading of the definitions. Consider Property (T1).

$$A_1 = T^{-1}(\cup B) = \{x: T(x) \in \cup B\}$$
$$A_2 = \cup T^{-1}(B) = \cup\{x: T(x) \in B\}$$

If $x \in A_1$, we must have $T(x)$ a member of $\cup B$. Hence $T(x) \in B$ for some set B_0 in the class. Thus

$$x \in \{x: T(x) \in B_0\} \subset \{x: T(x) \in \cup B\}$$

Because x is an arbitrary member of A_1, we conclude that $A_1 \subset A_2$.

To show the opposite inclusion relation, we suppose $x \in A_2$. Then we must have $x \in T^{-1}(B_1)$, where B_1 is some particular member of the class. This is the same as saying $T(x) \in B_1 \subset \cup B$, so that $x \in A_1$. Having established that $A_2 \subset A_1$, we have completed the proof of the equality.

Proofs of the other two statements may be carried out in a similar manner.

Although T was introduced as a point function or transformation, it is convenient to use the notation $T(A)$, where A is a subset of U, in the following manner:

$$T(A) = \{y: y = T(x) \text{ for some } x \in A\}$$

That is, $T(A)$ is the set of all the image points y for object points x in A. We may assert the following property:

(T4) $T(T^{-1}(B)) = B$

If we suppose that each set A in the following expressions is of the form

$T^{-1}(B)$ for some set $B \subset V$, we may assert

(T5) $T(\cup A) = \cup T(A)$

(T6) $T(\cap A) = \cap T(B)$

(T7) $T(A^c) = [T(A)]^c$

Proofs of these properties follow easily from the definitions and Properties (T1) through (T4). For example, consider the proof of (T7). We have

$$A^c = [T^{-1}(B)]^c = T^{-1}(B^c) \qquad \text{by } (T3)$$
$$T(A^c) = TT^{-1}(B^c) = B^c \qquad \text{by } (T4)$$
$$[T(A)]^c = [TT^{-1}(B)]^c = B^c \qquad \text{by } (T4)$$

We may utilize the properties above to establish one theorem which is important in the theory of probability. Suppose $\mathcal{B}$ is a completely additive class of sets B in the space V. The class $\mathcal{A}$ of sets A of the form $A = T^{-1}(B)$ for any B in $\mathcal{B}$ is then an additive class. The following arguments show closure of $\mathcal{A}$ under the formation of unions and complements.

$$\overset{\infty}{\underset{k=1}{\cup}} A_k = \overset{\infty}{\underset{k=1}{\cup}} T^{-1}(B_k)$$
$$= T^{-1}(\overset{\infty}{\underset{k=1}{\cup}} B_k) \text{ belongs to } \mathcal{A} \text{ since } \overset{\infty}{\underset{k=1}{\cup}} B_k \text{ belongs to } \mathcal{B}$$
$$A^c = [T^{-1}(B)]^c = T^{-1}(B^c) \text{ belongs to } \mathcal{A} \text{ since } B^c \text{ belongs to } \mathcal{B}$$

Suppose f is a function from an abstract space U to the real line R. Let M be any Borel set on the real line (Sec. 5-2). The class of Borel sets is a completely additive class. Then the class $\mathcal{A}$ of sets of the form $f^{-1}(M)$ for any Borel set is a completely additive class. Such classes arise in dealing with random variables in probability theory.

5-4. *Cartesian Product Spaces*

In this section we extend the treatment of cartesian product sets begun in Sec. 1-5. We deal with more complicated spaces and consider several types of sets useful in analysis.

Consider an arbitrary class $\{U_\alpha\}$, $\alpha \in I$, of coordinate spaces, with I an arbitrary index set (finite, countably infinite, or uncountably infinite). We denote by x_α an element of the coordinate space U_α. The cartesian product of the coordinate spaces is indicated by the symbol U_I, and the elements of this space are indicated by $x_I = \{x_\alpha\}$, $\alpha \in I$.

Let $\{J,K\}$ be a partition of the index set I and consider the cartesian products U_J and U_K. We identify the spaces U_I and $U_J \times U_K$. This amounts to identifying the elements x_I and the pairs of elements (x_J, x_K). We may illustrate this by letting $I = \{1,2,3,4,5\}$, $J = \{1,3,5\}$, and $K = \{2,4\}$. Then $x_I = (x_1, x_2, x_3, x_4, x_5)$, $x_J = (x_1, x_3, x_5)$, and

$$x_K = (x_2, x_4)$$

The element of $U_J \times U_K$ is of the form $[(x_1, x_3, x_5), (x_2, x_4)]$ which we

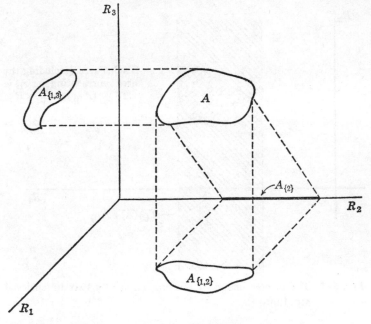

Fig. 5-2 Projections of a set in three-space.

identify with the element x_I having the same coordinates. The indexing serves to identify the coordinates, so that the reordering with respect to position is of no consequence.

Let A be a subset of U_I. We define the *J-projection transformation* T_J by the expression

$$T_J(A) = A_J = \{x_J \in U_J : (x_J, x_K) \in A \text{ for some } x_K \in U_K\}$$

The set A_J, which is a subset of U_J, is called the *J-projection* of A.

As a simple example, consider the three-dimensional set in Fig. 5-2.

Every point in the set $A_{\{1,2\}}$ has the property that there is a point of A "above" it.   This means that if we pick a pair of coordinates x_1 and x_2 which determine a point in $A_{\{1,2\}}$, at least one coordinate x_3 may be chosen so that the point (x_1,x_2,x_3) lies in A.   Similar statements hold concerning the other projections, as an examination of the figure will show.

It should be apparent that the projection of A into R_2 is the same as the projection of $A_{\{1,2\}}$ or $A_{\{2,3\}}$ (not shown on the figure) into R_2.

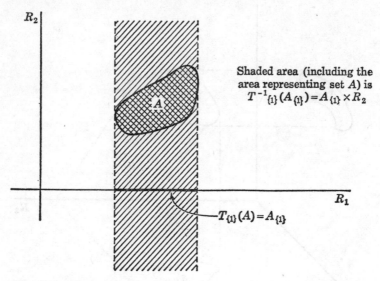

Fig. 5-3   The inverse image of the projection of a two-dimensional set A into R.

The result of a succession of projections to spaces of successively lower dimension is the same as a single projection from the space U_1 to the lowest dimensional space upon which the final projection is made.

Although the statement of the definition of the projection transformation is in terms of sets, it could have been stated as a point transformation.   There is a corresponding inverse transformation $T_J{}^{-1}$ which is defined by

$$T_J{}^{-1}(A_J) = \{x_I \in U_I : T_J(x_I) \in A_J \subset U_J\}$$

It should be apparent that

$$T_J{}^{-1}(A_J) = A_J \times U_K$$

since only the J coordinates determine membership in the J-projection A_J. The K coordinates can be anything, which is equivalent to saying x_K may range through the whole of U_K. Figure 5-3 shows a simple example in two space. The set A is projected into R_1; the projection is a line segment. The inverse image of the projection is the set of all points which are projected onto the line segment. This is a strip in the plane.

We define next the *J-section of A determined by x_J* as follows

$$A(x_J) = \{x_K \in U_K : x_I = (x_J, x_K) \in A\}$$

Note that here x_J is fixed, although it may be arbitrarily chosen. A

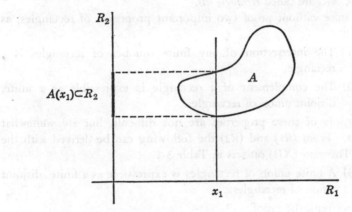

Fig. 5-4 A section of the plane set A determined by a
fixed value of the coordinate x_1.

simple example such as that in Fig. 5-4 will indicate the reason for referring to this type of set as a section.

In Sec. 1-5 the concept of a cylinder set is presented. We now generalize this definition. A set A in U_I is called a *J-cylinder* iffi altering those coordinates of an element whose indices are not in J cannot yield an element in A^c if x is in A, nor yield an element in A if x is in A^c. It follows that A is a J-cylinder iffi

$$A = T_J(A) \times U_K$$

It is apparent that $T_J^{-1}(A_J)$ is a *J-cylinder* for any set A, and that A is a J-cylinder iffi $A = T_J^{-1}(A_J)$. In view of this fact, we may apply Properties ($T1$) to ($T3$) for inverse transformations to obtain the following properties of cylinder sets:

(*C*1) $\cup T_J(A) \times U_K = [\cup T_J(A)] \times U_K$

(*C*2) $\cap T_J(A) \times U_K = [\cap T_J(A)] \times U_K$

(*C*3) $[T_J(A) \times U_K]^c = [T_J(A)]^c \times U_K$

It is worth noting in the above expression for Property (*C*3) that in general $T_J(A^c) \neq [T_J(A)]^c$. Reference to the example in Fig. 5-2 will show why this is so.

The concept of rectangle sets is introduced in Sec. 1-5 and may be generalized as follows. Suppose $\{J_1, J_2, \ldots, J_n\}$ is any finite partition of the index set I. We let $U_{(i)} = U_{J_i}$ for each $i = 1, 2, \ldots, n$, and let $A_{(i)}$ be a subset of $U_{(i)}$ for each i. Sets of the form $A_{(1)} \times A_{(2)} \times \ldots \times A_{(n)}$ are called *rectangle sets*.

We state without proof two important properties of rectangles, as follows:

(*R*1) The intersection of any finite number of rectangles is a rectangle.

(*R*2) The complement of a rectangle is expressible as a finite, disjoint union of rectangles.

The proofs of these properties are not difficult, but are somewhat tedious. From (*R*1) and (*R*2) the following can be derived with the aid of Theorem (*XII*) on sets in Table 3-1

(*R*3) A finite union of rectangles is expressible as a finite, disjoint union of rectangles.

Again we omit the proof.

It is of some interest to note that the class $\mathfrak{R}$ of all finite unions of rectangles is an additive class. It is obvious that the class is closed under the formation of finite unions. It remains only to show that the class is closed under the formation of complements. We consider the whole space U_I and the empty set $\emptyset$ as rectangles. Consider a set

$$A = \bigcup_{k=1}^{n} R_k$$

where each R_k is a rectangle set. Then

$$A^c = \bigcap_{k=1}^{n} R_k{}^c = \bigcap_{k=1}^{n} \bigcup_{j=1}^{m} R_{kj}$$

where each R_{kj} is a rectangle set. There is no loss of generality in assuming that each set $R_k{}^c$ is expressible as the union of the same number m of rectangles, for we can always use as many empty rectangles as we wish to fill out the number of terms. Now the intersection of the unions can be expressed as a union of intersections as follows:

$$\bigcap_{k=1}^{n} \bigcup_{j=1}^{m} R_{kj} = \bigcup R_{1j_1} R_{2j_2} \cdots R_{nj_n}$$

where each of the numbers j_1, j_2, . . . , j_n ranges over the values 1, 2, . . . , n. There are n^n product terms in the union, some of which may be empty. By Property $(R1)$ each product term is a rectangle, which verifies that A^c is included in the class of finite unions of rectangles. The class $\Re$ must therefore be an additive class.

Problems

5-1 Let $\{A_n\}$ be a sequence of sets. Show that there is a disjoint sequence $\{B_n\}$ such that

$$\bigcup_{n=1}^{\infty} A_n = \bigcup_{n=1}^{\infty} B_n$$

[Suggestion: See Theorem (XII), Table 3-1.]

5-2 If $\{A_n\}$ is any sequence of sets and we define

$$B_n = \bigcup_{k=n}^{\infty} A_k \quad \text{and} \quad C_n = \bigcap_{k=n}^{\infty} A_k$$

show that $\{B_n\}$ is a contracting sequence and that $\{C_n\}$ is an expanding sequence.

5-3 Show that any disjoint sequence $\{A_n\}$ is convergent and determine what its limit must be.

5-4 Show that

$$(\limsup A_n)^c = \liminf A_n^c$$
$$(\liminf A_n)^c = \limsup A_n^c$$

5-5 For any real number b, let

$$A(b) = \{x: x \leq b\}$$
$$A_n(b) = \left\{x: x < b + \frac{1}{n}\right\}$$

(a) Show that $A(b) = \lim A_n(b)$

(b) Show that $\{x: a < x \le b\} = \lim [A(a)]^c A_n(b)$
$$= [A(a)]^c \lim A_n(b)$$

5-6 Let U be a finite set with N elements. The class $\mathcal{C}$ consisting of all subsets of U has 2^N members. Show that $\mathcal{C}$ is a completely additive class.

5-7 Show that any additive class $\mathcal{C}$ with a finite number of members is a completely additive class.

5-8 Show that a nonempty class $\mathcal{C}$ closed under the formation of intersections and complements is an additive class.

5-9 Show that the completely additive class generated by all the closed intervals $[a,b]$ on the real line is the class of Borel sets.

5-10 Show that the completely additive class generated by all semi-infinite intervals of the form $(-\infty,a]$ is the class of Borel sets.

5-11 Consider a cartesian product space U_I as described in Sec. 5-4. Let L and J be subsets of I with L contained in J. Let T_J be the projection operator from U_I into U_J, let T_L be the projection operator from U_I into U_L, and let T_L^* be the projection operator from U_J into U_L. Show that for any set A in U_I

$$T_L(A) = T_L^*[T_J(A)]$$

5-12 Consider the cartesian product space U_I. Let $\{J,K\}$ be a partition of the index set. Consider the rectangle set $R = A_J \times B_K$.

(a) Show that $R = (A_J \times U_K)(U_J \times B_K)$.

(b) Show that $T_J(R) = A_J$ and $T_K(R) = B_K$.

(c) Show that the J-section $R(x_J)$ is either B_K or $\emptyset$, depending on the choice of x_J.

(d) Make a sketch illustrating the theorems for a rectangle set in the plane; i.e., let U_J and U_K each be the real line.

Bibliography

This bibliography is in no sense complete. A few of the works referred to are so basic that no such list would be complete without them. Most of the works, however, are included because they are both useful and typical. The bibliography could be extended severalfold with books and articles for which an equally strong argument for inclusion could be made. Some important and useful works have been omitted simply because they are more suited to the taste and/or the preparation of the advanced student of mathematics. Several of the books included have extensive bibliographies and lists of references, so that the brevity of the list herein provided need offer no serious obstacle to the reader interested in further study.

Readers interested in further study of various topics may find helpful the following guide to the bibliography by reference numbers.

Historical interest: Refs. 2, 7, 12, 14
Sets and algebra of set operations: Refs. 1, 4, 6, 9, 13, 15
Sets and events: Refs. 5, 7, 10
Probability: Refs. 5, 10
Indicator function (characteristic function): Ref. 10
Switching algebra and applications: Refs. 3, 8, 11, 15

1 Allendoerfer, C. B., and C. O. Oakley: "Principles of Mathematics," chap. 5, McGraw-Hill Book Company, Inc., New York, 1955.
2 Boole, George: "An Investigation of the Laws of Thought," London, 1854. Reprinted, Dover Publications, Inc., New York.

3 Caldwell, Samuel H.: "Switching Circuits and Logical Design," John Wiley & Sons, Inc., New York, 1958.

4 Davis, Robert L. (ed.): "Elementary Mathematics of Sets with Applications," Committee on the Undergraduate Program, Mathematical Association of America, 1958.

5 Goldberg, Samuel: "Probability: An Introduction," chaps. 1, 2, Prentice-Hall, Inc., Englewood Cliffs, N.J., 1960.

6 Kemeny, John G., Hazleton Mirkil, J. Laurie Snell, and Gerald L. Thompson: "Finite Mathematical Structures," chaps. 1, 2, Prentice-Hall, Inc., Englewood Cliffs, N.J., 1959.

7 Kolmogorov, A. N.: "Foundations of the Theory of Probability," 2d English edition, Chelsea Publishing Company, New York, 1956. English translation of "Grundbegriffe der Wahrscheinlichkeitsrechnung," Springer, Berlin, 1933.

8 Ledley, Robert S.: "Digital Computer and Control Engineering," chaps. 10, 11, McGraw-Hill Book Company, Inc., New York, 1960.

9 McShane, E. J.: Operating with Sets, in "Insights into Modern Mathematics," Twenty-third Yearbook, The National Council of Teachers of Mathematics, Washington, D.C., 1957.

10 Parzen, Emanuel: "Modern Probability Theory and Its Applications," chap. 1, John Wiley & Sons, Inc., New York, 1960.

11 Phister, Montgomery, Jr.: "Logical Design of Digital Computers," John Wiley & Sons, Inc., New York, 1958.

12 Shannon, Claude E.: "A Symbolic Analysis of Relay and Switching Circuits," *Trans. AIEE*, vol. 57, pp. 713–723, 1938.

13 Stabler, E. R.: "An Introduction to Mathematical Thought," Addison-Wesley Publishing Company, Inc., Reading, Mass., 1953.

14 Venn, John: "Symbolic Logic," The Macmillan Company, New York, 1894.

15 Whitesitt, J. Eldon: "Boolean Algebra and Its Applications," Addison-Wesley Publishing Company, Inc., Reading, Mass., 1961.

Appendix I

The Binary Number System

We ordinarily represent numbers in the *decimal number system*. When we write the symbols 342.75, for example, we indicate the number

$$3 \cdot 10^2 + 4 \cdot 10^1 + 2 \cdot 10^0 + 7 \cdot 10^{-1} + 5 \cdot 10^{-2} = 300 + 40 + 2 \\ + \tfrac{7}{10} + \tfrac{5}{100}$$

The expansion is in powers of 10. Each power of 10 is multiplied by one of the ten integers 0 through 9. The power of 10 is indicated by the *place* in the symbol representing the number. The coefficient of the kth power of 10 is put in the kth place. The number 10 is referred to as the *base* or the *radix* for the decimal system.

It is not necessary and sometimes not desirable to use the radix 10. Any integer—say 7 or 12—may be used. The simplest and most satisfactory system for many purposes is the *binary number system*, which uses radix 2. Coefficients for the various powers—designated by the appropriate place—are either 0 or 1. Thus, the binary number

$$101010110.11 = 1 \cdot 2^8 + 1 \cdot 2^6 + 1 \cdot 2^4 + 1 \cdot 2^2 + 1 \cdot 2^1 + 1 \cdot 2^{-1} + 1 \cdot 2^{-2}$$
$$= 256 + 64 + 16 + 4 + 2 + \tfrac{1}{2} + \tfrac{1}{4}$$
$$= 342\tfrac{3}{4} = 342.75$$

This is the same number as represented in the decimal system, above. The general scheme for representation of a number t is expressible as a series expansion in terms of powers of the radix as follows:

$$t = \sum_k \delta_k 2^k \qquad \text{where } \delta_k \text{ is 0 or 1}$$
$$= \sum_i a_i 10^i \qquad \text{where } a_i \text{ is 0, 1, 2, \ldots, 8, or 9}$$

Binary addition (two numbers at a time) is carried out quite simply as in the following example:

$$
\begin{array}{rcl}
110010 &=& 32 + 16 + 2 = 50 \\
\underline{10110} &=& 16 + 4 + 2 = \underline{22} \\
1001000 & & 72
\end{array}
$$

Addition in the kth place involves the two digits in the terms of the sum and a digit representing a carry from the result of addition in the $k - 1$ place. Each 1 in the kth place corresponds to 2^k. To add, count the 1s in the kth place, including the carry digit.

One 1 means the sum in the kth place is 2^k. Write sum 1 and carry 0.

Two 1s means the sum in the kth place is $2 \cdot 2^k = 2^{k+1}$. Write sum 0 and carry 1 into the $k + 1$ place (call this the kth carry).

Three 1s means the sum in the kth place is $3 \cdot 2^k = 2^{k+1} + 2^k$. Write sum 1 and carry 1.

The operations are detailed in the addition table, in which A_n and B_n are the nth place digits for the two numbers to be added, and C_{n-1} is the carry digit resulting from the addition in the $(n - 1)$th place.

Addition Table

C_{n-1}	A_n	B_n	C_n	S_n
0	0	0	0	0
0	0	1	0	1
0	1	0	0	1
0	1	1	1	0
1	0	0	0	1
1	0	1	1	0
1	1	0	1	0
1	1	1	1	1

Multiplication is extremely simple. Multiplication of a binary number by 2^j (i.e., a 1 in the jth place) moves all digits in the number to the left j places for j positive and $-j$ places to the right for j negative. This may be seen by noting that

$$2^j \left(\sum_k \delta_k 2^k \right) = \sum_k \delta_k 2^{k+j}$$

The integer δ_k is moved from the kth place to the $(k + j)$th place.

The product of two binary numbers is given by

$$\left(\sum_k \delta_k 2^k \right) \left(\sum_j \beta_j 2^j \right) = \sum_j \beta_j \left(\sum_k \delta_k 2^{k+j} \right)$$

Thus a simple "shift and add" algorithm provides multiplication. As an example, consider

$$
\begin{array}{rcl}
1001 & = & 9 \\
101 & = & 5 \\
\hline
1001 & & \\
0000 & & \\
1001 & & \\
\hline
101101 & = & 45
\end{array}
$$

It is obviously unnecessary to write the 0 products and add. Also, it is usually easier to perform the addition after each shift-and-write step.

An inversion of the process of multiplication provides a long-division procedure. We illustrate by carrying out the division 45/5, which inverts the multiplication above.

$$
\begin{array}{r}
1001 \\
101 \overline{)101101} \\
\underline{101} \\
000101 \\
\underline{101} \\
000
\end{array}
$$

We will not examine various tricks of the binary arithmetic which are exploited in modern digital computers, since the facts above more than serve the purpose of this monograph.

When binary representations are used (as in the function designation number of Sec. 3-5) it is helpful to know the value of each place. A table of values can be constructed quickly by noting that $2^{n+1} = 2 \cdot 2^n$, so that each successive entry in the 2^n table is twice the previous one. The first 16 values are tabulated below for convenience.

n	2^n	n	2^n	n	2^n	n	2^n
0	1	4	16	8	256	12	4,096
1	2	5	32	9	512	13	8,192
2	4	6	64	10	1,024	14	16,384
3	8	7	128	11	2,048	15	32,768

The Mathematical Concept of Relation

The intuitive concept of *relation* has been given a precise meaning in modern mathematics. This concept can be formulated in terms of sets in a manner quite similar to the formulation of the idea of *function*. In fact, as we note below, a function is a particular kind of relation. The similarity of the set-theoretic formulation of the concept of relation to that of *event* is also worth noting; this connection provides a further example of the manner in which the notion of set has been used to bring order and unity into diverse and seemingly unrelated aspects of mathematics.

What is meant by the question, "Does x stand in a given relation to y?" The question is addressed to a pair of entities (x, y). If a certain proposition is true concerning the pair, the relation is said to hold. Suppose we indicate the proposition by the symbol $*$. The expression $x * y$ then stands for the proposition "x stands in the given relation to y." Some simple examples will illustrate the usage.

    (i) If x and y are real numbers, we may let $*$ stand for the statement "is less than," in which case the expression $x * y$ is to be read "x is less than y." In this case, we have a special symbol commonly used for the statement; namely, the sign $<$. When we write $x < y$ we indicate symbolically the statement "x is less than y."

(ii) If x and y are subsets of the space U, we may let $*$ represent the statement "is contained in" or, equivalently, "is a subset of." Thus, $x * y$ means "x is contained in y." Again, we have a special symbol $\subset$ which is used with sets, so that we write $x \subset y$ rather than $x * y$.

(iii) If x and y are two human beings, we may let $*$ stand for the statement "is a child of." Thus, $x * y$ is read "x is a child of y." In this case, we have no generally recognized symbol.

Now if $x * y$ stands for a proposition concerning a pair of elements x and y of suitable universal sets (they may or may not be the same set), we say the relation holds iffi (x,y) is one of the pairs of elements for which $x * y$ is a true statement. The *relation* is described precisely and completely when the *set* of pairs (x,y) for which $x * y$ is true is determined. To determine if the relation holds, we determine whether the pair in question belongs to the describing set.

From the point of view just discussed, it is entirely natural to identify the relation R with the set of pairs (x,y) such that $x * y$ is true. In symbols

$$R = \{(x,y): x * y\}$$

We are thus led to make the abstract definition: A *relation* is a subset R of the cartesian product $U \times V$ of two spaces U and V which have elements x and y, respectively. The statement $x * y$ is a statement that is true of those pairs (x,y) in R and of no others. It is customary to refer to the relation R as the $*$ relation. For example, the relation determined by the proposition "is less than" is referred to as the "less than" relation or the $<$ relation.

A comparison of the above definition with that of a function given in Sec. 2-1 shows that a function f is a relation. We ordinarily use a different notational scheme for functions. Instead of writing $x * y$, we write $f(x) = y$. The distinguishing feature of a function is that it is single valued. This means that to each x in the domain set (a subset of U) there corresponds one and only one y in V. This is not true of relations in general, however. In the $<$ relation, for example, there is an infinity of values of y corresponding to each x.

To each relation R corresponds an *inverse relation* R^{-1}. A pair (y,x) belongs to R^{-1} iffi (x,y) belongs to R. Associated with the statement $*$ for

R there corresponds an inverse statement $*^{-1}$ for R^{-1}. Let us examine again the illustrative examples considered above:

Relation R		Inverse Relation R^{-1}	
Statement	$x * y$	$y *^{-1} x$	Inverse statement
x is less than y	$x < y$	$y > x$	y is greater than x
x is contained in y	$x \subset y$	$y \supset x$	y contains x
x is a child of y	$x * y$	$y *^{-1} x$	y is a parent of x

Relations may be studied in terms of several important properties. We consider briefly three basic properties.

(i) A relation is said to be *reflexive* on a set A iffi (x,x) is in R for each x in A; i.e., iffi the proposition $x * x$ is true for each x in A.

The relation $\leq$ is reflexive but the relation $<$ is not. The relation $\subset$ between subsets of a space is reflexive, but the relation "is a child of" between human beings is not.

(ii) A relation is said to be *transitive* iffi $x * y$ and $y * z$ implies $x * z$.

The relation "is a descendant of" is transitive but the relation "is a child of" is not transitive. The relation $<$ and the relation $\leq$ are both transitive.

(iii) A relation is said to be *symmetric* iffi $x * y$ implies $y * x$.

The relation $=$ is symmetric but the relation $\leq$ is not. The relation "is a next door neighbor to" among people is symmetric but the relation "is a child of" is not.

A relation which is transitive and which has the property that $x * y$ and $y * x$ are never both true for different elements is called a *partial ordering*. The relation $<$ for real numbers and the relation "is a refinement of" for partitions of a given set are partial orderings.

A relation which is reflexive, transitive, and symmetric is called an *equivalence relation*. The relation $=$ for real numbers is an equivalence relation. The following examples [Ref. 4, p. 58] are instructive and of some importance in themselves, for they show a connection between an equivalence relation on a set $E \times E$ and the idea of a partition of the set E.

Let $\mathcal{P}(E) = \{E_1, E_2, \ldots, E_n\}$ be any partition of E. Define a relation R on $E \times E$ by the expression

$$R = \{(x,y): x \text{ is in the same cell as } y\}$$

Then R is an equivalence relation, for obviously R is reflexive, transitive, and symmetric.

Now suppose we start with the set E and let R be any equivalence relation on $E \times E$. For any x in E let

$$E_x = \{ y \in E: (x,y) \in R \}$$

The distinct sets in the class $\{E_x\}$, $x \in E$, form a partition of E. This partition may have uncountably many members (in contrast to the finite or countable partitions considered previously). That the distinct sets in the class form a partition is a consequence of the following two assertions: (1) every y in E belongs to at least one E_x; and (2) two sets E_x and E_y are either identical or are disjoint. The class of distinct sets is thus a disjoint class whose union is E.

Index